ROYAL COLLEGE OF ART SCHOOLS TECHNOLOGY PROJECT

D&T ROUTES

FOOD

DESIGN & TECHNOLOGY 14–16

A TC Trust programme sponsored and supported by the Royal College of Art, the Esmée Fairbairn Trust, the Garfield Western Foundation and the Department for Education and Employment

Hodder & Stoughton

A MEMBER OF THE HODDER HEADLINE GROUP

Acknowledgements

The team: David Perry (Project Director), Louise T Davies (Deputy Project Director), Anthony R Booth (Assistant Project Director), Jim Sage (Assistant Project Director), Doris Massiah (Project Assistant), Imelda Rafter-Phillips (Admin Support). Main writers: Jan Barrow, Sarah Blake, Sian Cocks, Anne Constable, Ali Farrell, Terry Fiehn, Corrine Harper, Jenny Jupe, Barbara Mottershead, Robin Pellatt, Shirlee Posner.

Teacher fellows: Alan Booth, Claire Buxton, Anne Constable, Corrine Harper, Mark Hudson, Dai James, Mary Moran, Barbara Mottershead, Robin Pellatt, Rob Petrie, Brian Russell, Kalvin Turner.

Our special thanks to all contributing authors, including teacher fellows and their schools, and particularly their colleagues, partners, friends and children who have supported them while they were writing to meet deadlines.

The Royal College of Art Schools Technology Project wishes to extend its thanks to the following for their help and support in the writing of this book: Kathleen Lund (Chief Executive) and her colleagues at the T.C. Trust, the Department for Education and Employment, Office for Standards in Education (OFSTED), The Royal College of Art and their representatives on the Project Management Group.

Special thanks to: Roy Ballam, Stephanie Valentine, BNF; Carole Smith, National Dairy Council; Fraser Taylor, Findus Marketing; Janet Inglis.

Companies: Birds Eye Walls, Camden Food RA, Cauldron Foods, Cow & Gate Co, Dohler UK, Economatics, Findus, Greenhalgh Bakery, Health Education Authority/Marston Book Services Ltd, Lloyd Instruments, Lucas Ingredients, McVities, Nestlé, Nutrition Task Force (NTF), Pennine Foods, Research Association, RHM Technology, Rooster Foods, Scotia Haven, St. Martins Foods, J. Sainsbury.

The illustrations were drawn by: Maggie Brand of the Maggie Mundy Agency; Hardlines Design and Illustration, Tom Cross Illustration and Design and Sally Artz. Book design by Lynda King. The Cover illustrations were drawn by Danny Jenkins of fab 4 studio.

The publishers would like to thank the following individuals, institutions and companies for permission to reproduce copyright material in this book. Every effort has been made to trace ownership of copyright. The publishers would be happy too make arrangements with copyright holders whom it has not been possible to contact.

J Allan Cash Ltd. (32 right, 32 top left); Ambrosia (20 top left); Amoy (22 top right); armfield (66, 67 top); Birds Eye Wall's (20 bottom left, 77); John Birdsall (3 all, 15 top left and right, 37 top, 42 all, 44 right, 45 all, 60 right, 62 all, 64 both, 83 left, 84 middle); The Anthony Blake Photo Library (21 left, 26, 38 bottom right, 53); Chris Brown/Action-Plus (4 centre); Cauldron Foods Ltd. (91 all, 92, 93, 60 left); Andy Collison/The Anthony Blake Photo Library (9); Corporate Photography (89 top left); Coventry Evening Telegraph (6 bottom); CPC UK Ltd (4 left); Darius (27 bottom right); Dawn Foods (14 top); Dohler (15 middle); Findus (40 top); Neal Haynes/Action-Plus (7 right, 21 right); Elizabeth Hewitt (7 bottom left); Hodder Photo Library (15 bottom, 40 bottom, 55, 84 bottom); Roger Hutchings/Rex Features (24 right); James King-Holmes/Farmer Giles Foods/Science Photo Library (54, 68 bottom); James King-Holmes/Northern Foods/Science Photo Library (12 left, 65 bottom left, 74 top); Glyn Kirk/Action-Plus (4 centre top, 7 top left); Kitchen Range (20 top right); Kraft (20 bottom right); Leatherhead Food Research (89 top right, 88 bottom left); Emma Lee/Life File (4 bottom centre, 10 top, 30 left, 32 left, 52, 87 right); Lloyd Instruments (84 top, 83 top right); Damien Lovegrove/Science Photo Library (56); Professor Hal McFie (46 bottom, 51); McVitie's (61 left, 86); Peter Menzel/Science Photo Library (28 left); National Starch and Chemical Company (67 bottom, 68 top, 74 bottom, 87 left); New Covent Garden Soup Co. (36 both); Alan Newnham (18 right top and bottom); Oxoid (82); Thierry Perrin/Rex Features (30 right); Pin-it Pastry (50 bottom); QSA Ltd (78); Rex Features (24 left, 65 top left, top right); RHM Technology (15 top, 88 bottom); Rosenfeld Images/The Anthony Blake Photo Library (2, 12 right, 16 bottom, 28 right, 65 middle right, bottom left, 71); Peter Ryan/Science Photo Library (34 right); Safeway (22 top left); Jim Sage (84 top); Sainsbury's (18 left, 50 top, 61 left); Scotia Haven Foods (73); Systech Instruments (11, 83 bottom right, 88 top); The Anthony Blake Photo Library (21 left, 26, 38 bottom right, 53); Tingle/Action-Plus (4 right); Upie (37 bottom left); Virtuality (44 top left, bottom left); Williams Photography Ltd (45 top, 48 bottom); Xynergy (6 top); Yoplait (23); Ed Young/Agstock/Science Photo Library (65 middle left).

British Library Cataloguing in Publication Data
A catalogue record for this title is available from The British Library

Student Book
ISBN 0340 67392 3

First published 1997

Impression number	10	9	8	7	6	5	4	3	2	1
Year	2002	2001	2000	1999	1998	1997				

Teacher's Notes
ISBN 0 340 69733 4

First published 1997

Impression number	10	9	8	7	6	5	4	3	2	1
Year	2002	2001	2000	1999	1998	1997				

Typeset by Wearset, Boldon, Tyne and Wear.
Printed in Great Britain for Hodder & Stoughton Educational, a division of Hodder Headline Plc, 338 Euston Road, London NW1 3BH by Scotprint, Musselburgh, Scotland

Contents

Introduction

This book should be used with the *D&T Routes Students Core Book* which provides you with advice on how to organise and manage your work in D&T. It will help you to analyse and evaluate products, and with your designing and manufacturing. It will also increase your understanding of industrial approaches to manufacturing in a variety of materials which both GCSE D&T and GNVQ Manufacturing courses expect.

This book contains:

- three **Full Designing and Making Assignments (DMAs)** comprising a design and make Challenge together with supporting focused tasks and case studies
- six **Outline DMAs** which present you with a design and make Challenge and some starting points to help you get going
- **Designing and Manufacturing** sections with focused tasks, information and case studies that support your designing and making and increase your knowledge about industrial approaches
- a section on **The Business of Manufacturing** which will help to further develop your understanding of manufacturing. This is essential if you are following a GNVQ Manufacturing course but will also enhance your designing and making if you are on a GCSE D&T course.

You can use the DMAs as they stand or to help you to develop your own projects.

There are five focus area books in the *D&T Routes* series: *Resistant Materials*; *Food*; *Textiles*; *Control Products* and *Graphic Products*. You will find it useful to refer to the other books in the series.

Design and Technology produces products in various materials but there are common features in the designing processes and manufacturing processes used. If you are following a GCSE course with a narrower focus you should first think about what is special to your focus area.

Exploring and understanding the physical and chemical properties of food

What is food technology?

Food technology is about new product development. It relates to the practicalities of food preservation and the manufacture of a large variety of products. In school it involves many practices which are common in the food manufacturing industry, drawing on scientific understanding and the operation of food processing equipment.

Investigating and understanding nutritional, biological and sensory properties of foods

Exploiting the properties to design and manufacture food products

Fit food

Your challenge

There are many factors a **sports person** has to consider in order to be successful. The type of food that he or she eats affects their level of fitness. Many professional sports people have their own dietician to work on their dietary needs in relation to the performance required. Select a sport that you are interested in and investigate the **nutritional requirements** that assist in gaining peak performance in it.

Your challenge is to develop prototypes for a range of products designed specifically for a particular sport. You will need to consider how these prototypes would be made in **high volume**.

Why this activity is useful

You will understand how the food industry uses precise dietary requirements to promote and sell particular sporting activity foods to a very specialist niche market.

You will become aware of the range of such products on the market.

You will learn how the food industry balances the nutritional requirements of a product with other considerations such as taste, texture and keeping quality.

You will also raise your awareness of food additives and how they may be used to ensure that specific nutritional requirements are met.

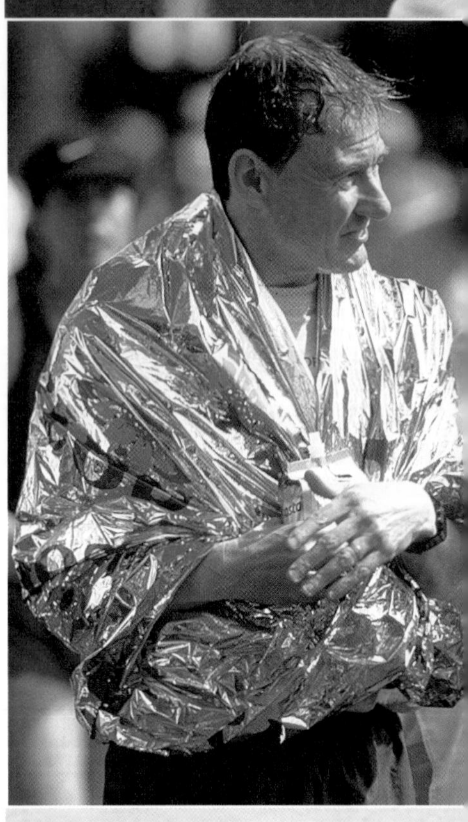

Values issues

Many food manufacturers are associated with various sports, mainly as a result of sponsorship deals. In groups, discuss how specific dietary products could aid performance. Identify a particular product and evaluate its relationship with an individual sport.

- Some people feel that a normal healthy well-balanced diet is appropriate for everyone and that sports people, and other groups of people targeted by the manufacturers, do not need specialist diets. What do you think?
- How effective is legislation in controlling the claims that manufacturers can make about their products?

To be successful

You will need to:

- Research one type of sport and its specific dietary requirements to help you formulate a precise product range specification.
- Use your knowledge of how food can be combined to make different types of products. Be creative and produce imaginative combinations.
- Produce a range of different foods and/or drinks, with detailed nutritional analysis, directly related to a particular sporting activity. Your products should be carefully formulated to help the user achieve peak performance.
- Evaluate your prototypes and assess both their appeal and value for a particular sport. Consider how the range will be made in high volume.

How to get going

- Firstly, identify a sport that you will be able to research. Make a detailed analysis of the sport and the needs of the user. Collect information from a variety of sources including sports magazines, specialist books and local experts such as dieticians or nutritionists. This research will help you formulate a specification for the range, identifying which features and nutritional requirements you feel are particularly relevant to your chosen sport. Use this research to develop your ideas.
- Allow time to generate a range of ideas. Examine the different sources of each nutrient and consider how different ingredients can be combined. Try your ideas out on the user and analyse each one for its nutritional content.
- Make a number of prototypes, evaluate and improve them to get to your final range of products.

Fit food

Looking at existing products

Work in a small group and collect a range of products which are aimed at the sports person. Carry out a product analysis investigation. You could make a chart with the following headings to record information about each product:

- What are the main ingredients?
- What is the purpose of each ingredient?
- Who is it for?
- What does it do?
- How is it made?
- When is it used?
- How much does it cost?
- How is it packaged?
- What is its shelf life?

You may also want to carry out a detailed sensory evaluation as taste, texture, colour and smell are of great importance.

- List the attributes you feel are most important for your sports person
- How can you incorporate these into your product?

Case study: Finding out what sports people need to eat

Many sports have certain performance criteria. Some of these can be developed by following an eating strategy which, with effective training, can help a sports person obtain peak performance. You will need to find out as much information as possible about your sport.

Teresa Davies

Scottish Senior Record Holder 200 m Butterfly

I always have a high carbohydrate diet, but during intense training, the amounts I eat gradually increase. One week before an event, most of the food that I eat consists of different complex carbohydrates.

During training sessions I have to constantly drink low sugar fruit juices that have salt added to them, in order to prevent dehydration.

Case study: Finding out what sports people need to eat – continued

Tim Henman

Top British tennis player

Eats 1 kg bananas a day to provide the energy he needs during long training sessions and matches.

Dominic Girdler

Has represented England in the schools pentathlon

Participating in a multi-event competition such as the pentathlon requires the production of two types of energy: quick bursts for sprinting, hurdling, jumping and throwing; and stamina for the middle distance running. During a competition, I have to constantly eat between events. Linford Christie recommended eating bananas and I have found them to provide the nutrients that I need. I also consume high energy snack bars and drinks.

Eugene Waldron

Basketball player for Leicester Riders

I must finish my meal four hours before the 'tip-off'. It always consists of lots of pasta or potatoes with chicken. A colleague eats two hours before a match, and he often suffers from a 'stitch' as digestion takes blood away from the muscles. Eating a heavy meal makes me feel bloated and unable to run around. Before and during a game I drink lots of water to replace lost body fluids.

Fit food

Food Facts

Carbohydrate loading

Carbohydrate "loading" was developed in Sweden in the 1960s. The aim is for the body to build up two to three times its normal stores of glycogen, in order to enhance endurance. Three days before an event, training will stop and the person will begin a carbohydrate loading regime, e.g. 500–600 g of simple carbohydrates in the first 24 hours, followed by a similar amount of mainly complex carbohydrates in the next 24 hours.

Simple or complex carbohydrates?

All carbohydrate, low fat foods are beneficial to athletic performance. Simple carbohydrates, e.g. sucrose, glucose and dextrose, provide an initial rush of energy and may speed recovery after strenuous exercise. However, for a sustained energy release, you need complex carbohydrates (polysaccharides), e.g. pasta, rice and bread.

Protein

Intensive training causes strain on muscle fibres which can be repaired by amino acids. Research has not proven how much protein is needed, or when, for peak performance, but it is recommended that high biological protein should be eaten as soon as possible after training. If a sports person has enough protein in their diet to meet their dietary needs (1–2 g per kg body weight for athletes) then it should not be necessary to increase the intake.

Hydration

Fluid intake and sodium replacement need to be regulated to maintain the body's fluid and electrolyte balance, to avoid dehydration and cramp. The recommendation is that sports people follow a plan for adequate rehydration during or after exercise.

Lactic acid

Lactic acid builds up when a person uses both aerobic and anaerobic energy production systems when exercising. An intake of bicarbonate of soda can neutralise the acid but "soda-loading" in high doses causes diarrhoea and stomach upsets.

Foods which cause a quicker rise in blood sugar (i.e. high glycaemic index)
Glucose, glucose confectionery (e.g. jelly beans/babies), honey
Some breakfast cereals (e.g. cornflakes, puffed rice)
Wholemeal and white bread
Rice noodles
Rice: brown and white
Some fruits: tropical, stewed fruits, ripe bananas
Some vegetables: parsnip, potato and pumpkin
Sports drinks, soft drinks and cordials

Foods which cause a slower, more sustained rise in blood sugar (i.e. low glycaemic index)
Pulses: dried beans, baked beans, peas and lentils
Oat, barley and bran cereals: porridge, muesli, bran flakes, wholegrain cereals
Breads with large amounts of wholegrains
All pastas
Basmati rice
Some fresh fruits: apples, cherries, grapefruit, oranges, peaches, pears, plums and firm bananas
Some vegetables: sweet potato, sweet corn
Barley, buckwheat, bulghur (e.g. tabbouleh)

Formulating a specification

You might like to build up a specification by producing a chart similar to the one below:

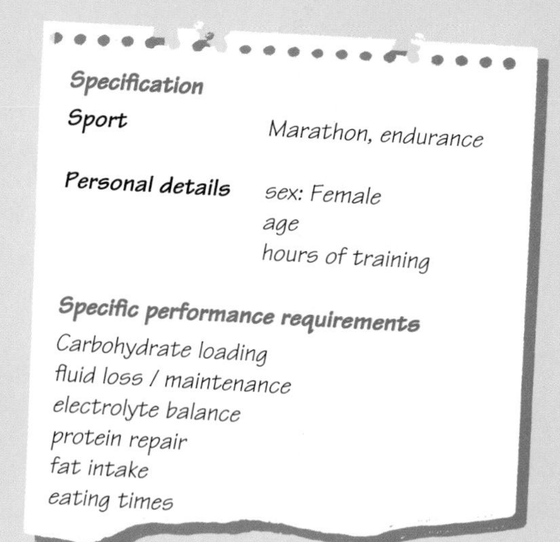

Specification

Sport	Marathon, endurance
Personal details	sex: Female age hours of training

Specific performance requirements

Carbohydrate loading
fluid loss / maintenance
electrolyte balance
protein repair
fat intake
eating times

Generating ideas

Using your list of nutritional information, create a recipe bank to enable trialling and testing for the development of your range of products.

Try to use unusual sources and combinations to create some novel food products.

Choosing the right food and combinations

Identify the sources of the nutrients you have specified and draw up a list of possible foods that will supply these. This will help you plan which ingredients you can use for your range of products. You might like to use a chart like the one below:

Nutrient	Sources	Possible uses
carbohydrate	pasta	various sauces, meats & vegetables dried snack food soups
protein	egg	scrambled, boiled quiches pastries aerated mixtures—mousses, cakes
sodium	table salt	bacon, fish & processed meats peanuts, crisps isotonic drinks

Considering other needs and wants

As well as nutritional considerations you will need to take into account the needs and wants of the consumer.

- When and where are they going to consume it?
- How much do they need to eat or like to eat (portion size)?
- What textures, colours, aromas and flavours appeal to them?
- How much are they willing to pay?
- How often will they want to buy it and how will they store it?

Use this information to build up a specification for each of the products in your range. These points may be helpful when evaluating each product you have trialled.

Energy bars

Risk assessment, D&T Routes Core Book page 84

Prototyping

Now get busy and try out some of your ideas by making them! Plan how you are going to make each product. You will probably need to follow a recipe or flow chart. Try out each product design and evaluate it against your specification. You may need to improve your recipe and try again.

Evaluating

Use your specification to make a list of the things which are important to your sports person. What will they be looking for when they buy a product? These are the things that you need to evaluate your product against. A successful product meets the needs of the user. How are you going to assess the things on your list?

Attribute	How to assess it
Taste	Set up a taste panel, or invite a sports person to try it over time and record their views on your product.
Nutritional content	Do a computer analysis of the nutritional content.
Cost	Use a spreadsheet to work out the unit cost

Assessing nutritional information

Calculate the amount of nutrients in your product.

Age	Estimated average requirements for energy in kJ (kcal)	
	Male	Female
7–10 years	8274 (1970)	7308 (1740)
11–14 years	9324 (2220)	7749 (1845)
15–18 years	11571 (2755)	8862 (2110)
19–50 years	10710 (2550)	8148 (1940)
51–59 years	10710 (2550)	7980 (1900)
60–64 years	9996 (2380)	7980 (1900)
65–74 years	9786 (2330)	7980 (1900)
75+ years	8820 (2100)	7602 (1810)
Pregnancy (last 3 months only)		Need an extra 840 (200)*
Breastfeeding 1 month		Need an extra 1890 (450)*

* These amounts should be added to the usual energy requirements, depending on the age, of a non-pregnant woman.

You will need to consider the actual quantities used, portion size and **dietary reference values**. Evaluate how well your product meets the nutritional needs of the sport. Will these products help the sports person gain peak performance? Suggest modifications that may be necessary in the light of your calculations.

Extra time?

If you want to be a winner in this project, you can always think of some additional tasks which will support your project:

- Present the results of your research to help sports people plan their eating better. This could be an information sheet, video or multi-media presentation.
- Prepare a presentation to make to a company about your product range.
- Produce ideas for packaging and nutritional labelling.
- Produce a plan for a manufacturer to follow to make your product in high volume.

Flexible manufacturing

Your challenge

The food industry is one of the largest **manufacturing** industries in Britain. There are many famous multi-national companies and also many small companies.

Imagine you are working for a small food company which has just installed equipment to provide them with flexible manufacturing throughout the year. As part of the **development team**, your **challenge** is to design a basic product that can have some of the processing continuing throughout the year and parts altered to provide **variations** both throughout the year and for special events.

Why this activity is useful

You will appreciate how food companies must use their plant efficiently, so that it is in use for the maximum amount of time possible.

You can investigate the use of pre-manufactured components.

It will help you understand high risk and low risk ingredients and their influence on the final product.

You can work out the cost of finishing products and the wastage involved.

You will gain an awareness of consumers' desire to try something "new".

Values issues

- The high cost of a product may be because of labour intensive preparation or finishing processes. How do you feel about paying more for some products? Which groups of people are more likely to put convenience before cost?
- Pre-manufactured food components help to cut labour charges but are designed to appeal to the average taste and may contain additives. Identify some of the additives used by the food industry and where they may be used.
- What do you think of marketing techniques that use events, such as the Olympic games, contemporary themes, movies, or famous people to sell the same product in a new package?

To be successful

- Imagine that you are the production manager and it is your responsibility to make sure that the factory works at maximum efficiency all the year round. Plan out the production run for the year. Be creative in your ideas for a whole year's production.
- You will need to develop a standard recipe and then consider the possible variations, e.g. additional ingredients, and alternative finishing such as decoration and garnish.
- You should design and make several high quality variations of your product.

How to get going

- Researching festivals from different cultures may help you find ideas.
- Foods may be associated with, or more plentiful at, particular times of the year.
- Supermarkets often produce leaflets about fruit and vegetables that state their availability and country of origin.
- You may need to allow time for practising decorative finishes to the products.
- Investigate the cost of using raw ingredients or pre-manufactured components.
- You might find it helpful to use a Gantt chart to show the production for a year.
- You will need to map out the unit operations to identify the standard operations and the variations.

Flexible manufacturing

Choosing your base product

This Challenge gives you a wide range of products to choose from. Here are some ideas.

Flexible products

A standard product may be altered in several ways

Different coatings
flavoured/coloured coating given to a cake
fillings and toppings for flans and pies
sauces to serve with meat, fish, vegetables or pasta

Different toppings
decorations on a cake
spray glazes for sweet and savoury biscuits
toppings for cheesecake

Added ingredients
spices and fruit added to bagels or bread products
herbs and spices in sauces, marinades and salad dressings

How could you alter your product?

- Use the examples above to help you with ideas for the whole year.
- Be creative, try putting unusual ingredients together.
- Think about:
  - themes
  - seasons
  - festivals and local traditions
  - special events.
- Record your ideas and ask people what they think of your ideas.

Case study: Peter Rabbit Cake modelled with software

RHM Technology models its ideas for different cake toppings using 3D modelling software.

RHM Technology uses 3D Modelling Studio® virtual reality software to produce photorealistic 3 dimensional images of design concepts. Here is an example of a Peter Rabbit cake being modelled.

Try using a modelling or CAD system to record and try out some of your ideas.

Pre-manufactured components

Counting the cost of variations

Hand finishing, such as counting the number of prawns, weighing the amount of chicken, adding delicate components such as chocolate leaves, using complicated decorating techniques, takes time and increases labour costs. This means that the production cost will be higher.

Note how much time you take to make the standard recipe and then the extra time required to make each variation.

- How can you speed up production to make it more efficient?
- How can you ensure that each product is of the same high standard?
- Can you use special equipment to help you?
- Will you need to simplify the design?
- Can you use pre-manufactured components?
- How can you minimise waste?

Some ingredients may not keep well. Fresh fruit toppings such as whole strawberries, raspberries and bananas will deteriorate quickly. Some ingredients may be very fragile and will need careful handling and special packaging.

Industry often buys in pre-manufactured food components. These produce a consistent product without relying on the skill of the operator.

- What pre-made components are available to you?
- You must decide which components are the most suitable for your products.

Carry out comparison tests between several types of components and the raw ingredients. Consider cost, time, wastage, effort, energy and quality of end product. Explain why you would recommend the use of a particular component.

Comparison for apple pie – use of a ready-made component!

Apples	Cost	Keeping quality	Time	Effort	Quality of end product
1. Fresh peeled apples 2. Frozen apple slices 3. Dried apple rings 4. Canned apple slices 5. Canned apple pie filling					

Could you manufacture your own components that could be used in several products?

Flexible manufacturing

Planning production

As production manager, you must map out the use of the production lines for the year. Use a chart to show how you will change the product throughout the year.

You must also consider the stages in production and what tooling implications there are because of the variations. You will need to make a basic list of equipment for the product and additional equipment needed for each variation.

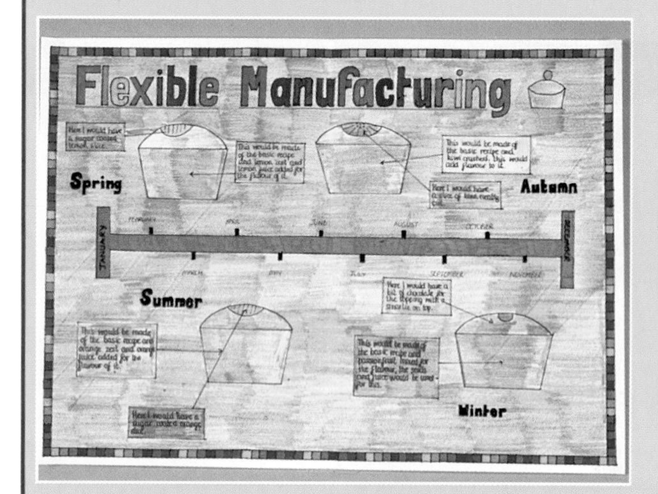

Draw a flow chart stating unit operations and identify the stages where changes will need to be made.

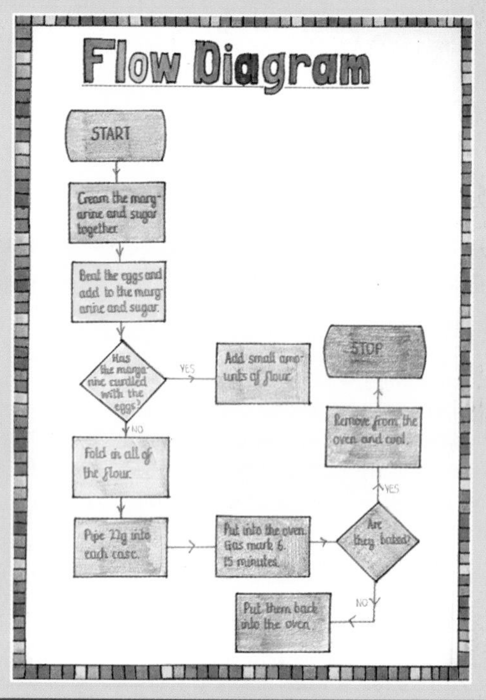

High risk and low risk foods

Certain foods provide better conditions for the growth of food poisoning (**pathogenic**) bacteria than others. Extra care must be taken when these foods are being handled.

Find out about the main pathogenic bacteria, their sources, growing conditions and the foods associated with them. You can use this information to identify all the risks and use preventative measures when planning a production line.

Reported food vehicles in general outbreaks of food poisoning in England and Wales 1989–1991 (where causative food identified)

Type of food	Number of general outbreaks
Chicken	41
Turkey	28
Other poultry	1
Beef	29
Pork or Ham	20
Cold meats	7
Lamb or Mutton	9
Other meats or pies	53
Gravy or sauces	2
Milk	3
Other dairy products	3
Eggs	52
Rice	20
Vegetables or spices	3
Bakery products	7
Sweets or puddings	26
Mixed foods	95
Shellfish	1

Source: How to HACCP, 2nd Edition, pub 1996

High risk and low risk foods – continued

Main pathogenic micro-organisms with sources in nature and the foods they are mainly associated with

Micro-organisms	Source in nature	Associated foods
Salmonella spp.	Water, soil, mammals, birds, insects intestinal tracts of animals, especially poultry and pigs.	Beef, turkey, pork, chicken eggs and products, meat salads, crabs, shell-fish, chocolate, animal feeds, dried coconut, baked goods and dressings.
Listeria monocytogenes	Soil, silage, water and other environmental sources, birds, mammals, and possibly fish and shellfish.	Raw milk, soft cheese, coleslaw, ice-cream, raw vegetables, raw meat sausages, raw and cooked poultry, raw and smoked fish, pâté.
Campylobacter jejuni	Soil, sewage, sludge, untreated waters, intestinal tracts of chickens, turkeys, cattle, swine, rodents and some wild birds.	Raw milk, chicken, other meats and meat products.
Staphylococcus aureus	Hands, throats and nasal passages of humans; common on animal hides.	Ham, turkey, chicken, pork, roast beef, eggs, salads (e.g. egg, chicken, potato, macaroni), bakery products, cream-filled pastries, luncheon meats, milk and dairy products.

Using your list of ingredients, highlight the ones that are high risk.

Now consider the state of the foods, raw or cooked and their position within the whole production line.

Draw a flow chart for your product starting with the input of the raw materials to the output of the finished product. Clearly identify the high risk areas.

Flow chart for ravioli

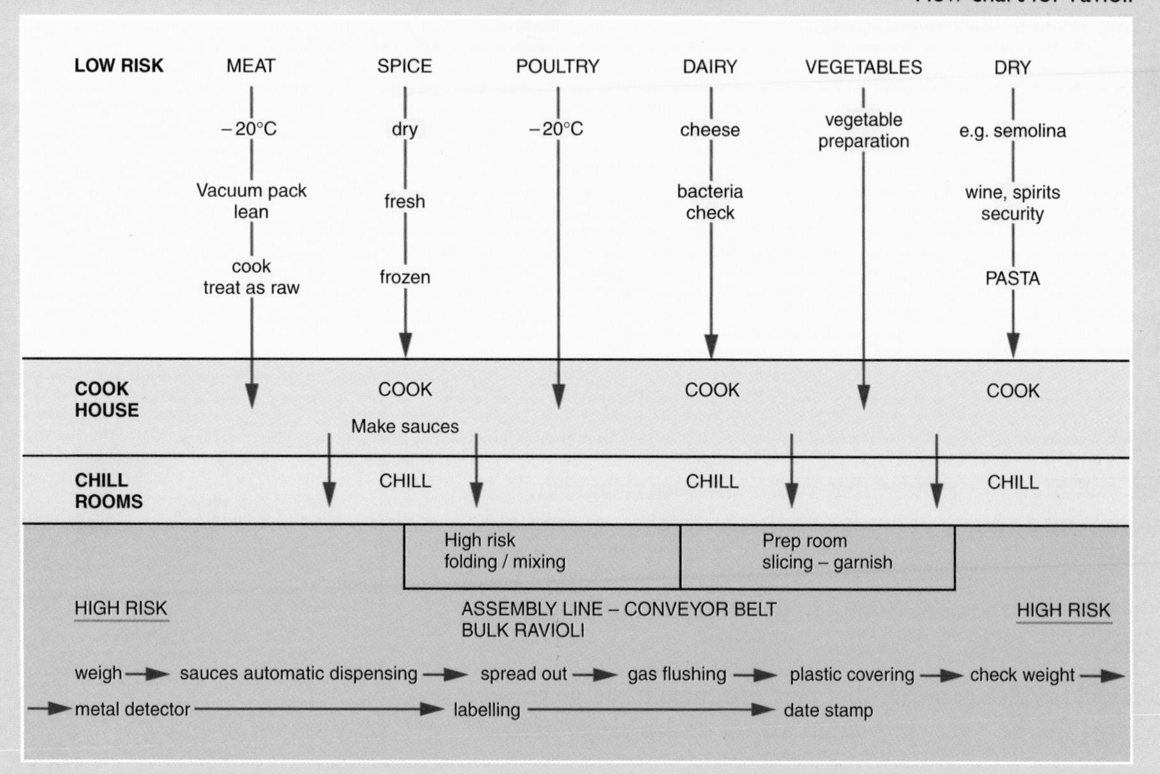

Pack it away

Your challenge

Every day millions of people pack food into containers so that they can eat it later in the day. "Take a piece", "Have a shivery-bite" (a swimming snack), "pack-up", "picnic" are all names given to this kind of food.

Your challenge is to design and make products which are suitable for a packed meal aimed at a particular **event or occasion**. You might like to develop the whole range of products yourself or work as part of a team.

Every product must be tried and tested. It is important that these products are the right **portion size**. They should also keep well and still look and taste good when transported.

Why this activity is useful

You will learn how companies develop products for a particular target audience.

You will need to consider that companies are increasingly assembling a variety of foods to help us develop a complete menu.

You will have the opportunity to develop a coordinated menu of foods.

You will need to consider that new products undergo travel tests and this will be a very important aspect of this range of foods.

Values issues

- Packaging materials can create many problems; describe any that you have encountered in packed meals that you have bought.
- Can you design a product which has minimal or even edible packaging?
- Companies spend considerable amounts of money developing luxury and special occasion foods. How do you feel about this when faced with the fact that some people have very little food?
- How can you ensure that you are encouraging people to eat more healthily?

To be successful

- Identify a suitable context and link both food and container to the event and the target market.
- Products should be appropriate to the context, they should complement one another and be in appropriate portion sizes.
- Investigate how different ingredients and mixtures will withstand transportation and packaging. Suggest a novel way of packaging the meal that is compact and efficient.

How to get going

- Develop your ideas by finding out what products, packaging materials and concepts are already on the market.
- Capture the context on a mood board.
- Allow time to try out the ideas and assess their suitability to the context.
- Consider the feasibility of packaging your products in school.
- Evaluate each product for quality in relation to time and travel.

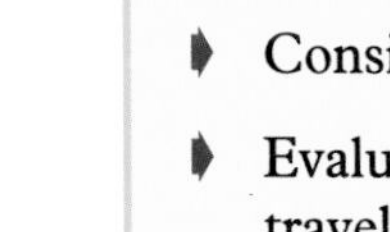

Pack it away

Case study: Designing for a target market

There are thousands of products suitable for packed meals on the market, but recently manufacturers have produced items tailor-made for specific situations and specific target groups. You could carry out some product analysis to see what has already been designed and made.

D&T Routes Core Book
page 28

Ambrosia desserts in pots include rice pudding, custard and flavoured milk-based desserts. They do not need refrigeration and are perfect for lunch-boxes.

The Lost World ice-lolly is the most detailed and colourful 3D water ice that Wall's has ever made. The lurid green and yellow Tyrannosaurus Rex head conceals a raspberry flavoured blood-red gooey centre.

Kitchen Range Green Goo! is a novel pastry product. Green Goo! is aimed at the children's market and features a crispy pastry pie case and a green filling tasting of banana. It is designed to be eaten as a hand held snack.

Kraft Handisnacks are cheesy dips partnered with savoury breadsticks, crackers or chipsticks and packaged in twin pots.

Choosing a situation or context

Discuss the different situations for which a packed meal could be developed. You may like to make a chart to list different events, people, and time to help you decide on a suitable context.

Events	People	Time
Working meal	any	any
Swimming	toddler	lunch
	competitor	breakfast
Rock festival	teenager	all day
Celebration	any	any
Birthday		
Graduation		
Sport		

What will they want?

Food companies research carefully, and are very precise about producing the food for a specific target group. They consider social, cultural, ethical and economic values and trends.

Use the triangle approach below to help you identify your target audience more accurately.

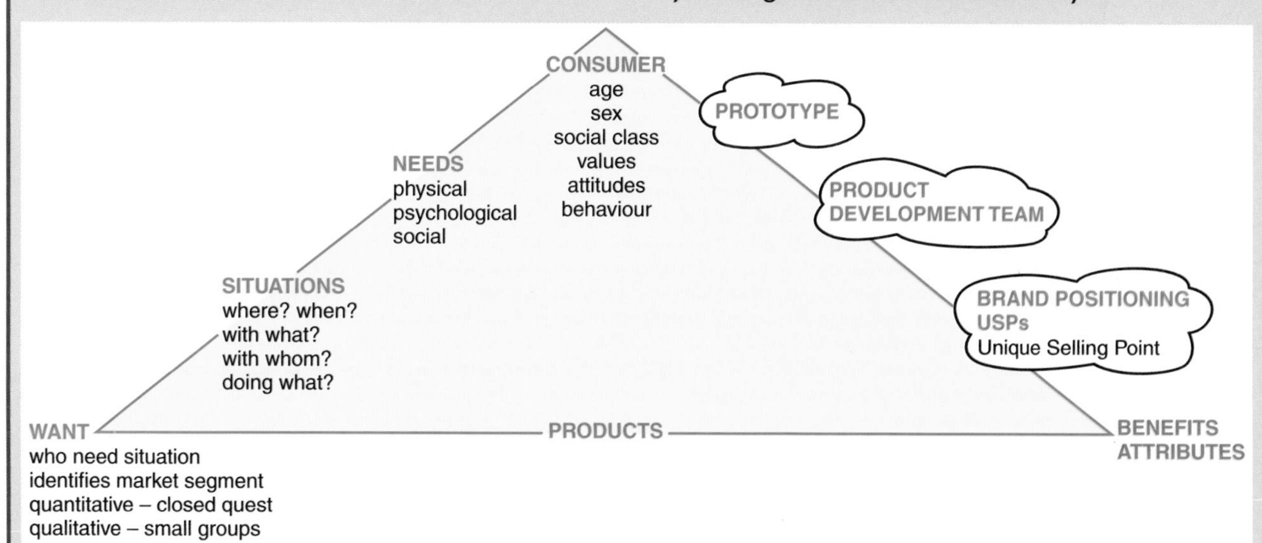

Pack it away

Developing ideas

From your chosen context and target audience, draw up a list of criteria that will enable you to develop ideas for your meal.

You may find it useful to consider the following:

- the variety of textures, colours, flavours, aromas
- portion sizes
- cost
- transportation of the food
- an overview of the whole meal

You may want to create a mood board to help you.

Ready to eat or ready to cook?

- Will you design products which are ready to eat or will they be ready to cook? (Whichever you choose, it will be important that the product is of high quality. Hygiene and safety regulations must be followed.)
- How will you make sure the food is safe?
- What packaging materials can you use?
- Will you need to make sure some foods are kept separate because of cross contamination or strong smell?
- How will you protect fragile ingredients?

Portion control

Food companies work out the portion size accurately because if food is wasted, the company's profit may be reduced.

Transportation and personal requirements will also affect the size and shape of each food item within your meal. Explore the range of possibilities for each part of the meal.

A quiche could be round, square or oblong, or sliced in various sizes. Different shapes and sizes affect how easily the product can be packaged and transported

The quantity required by each person may also be different

Portion control – continued

Work out the cost of the portion. Look at other products: do supermarkets charge more for smaller portions?

Looking good and tasting good

You will need to check that your ideas keep well and travel well. How might you set up a test to show this?

Design a fair test to decide which wrapping is best to use. Interview your customers to check which packages appeal to them most.

Case study: Petits Filous 'Frubes'

Only 6.3% of children's fromage frais was eaten as a snack until Petits Filous developed 'Frubes'. The convenience and 'snackability' of Frubes enable children to eat them anywhere. The lack of a spoon was the main reason given by parents for not adding fromage frais to their children's lunchboxes. Spoons placed in lunchboxes were rarely returned!

During the design development, there were some problems to be overcome:

- If fromage frais was left in tanks too long before filling the tubes, it would separate
- The packs did not always open along the tear line
- Frubes had to be packed by hand.

Survival

Your challenge

Life can be comfortable – many of us may never have to survive in a life-threatening situation or environment. However, to test their survival skills, some people choose to put themselves into high-risk situations under controlled conditions.

Unfortunately, too many people across the world find themselves in desperate survival situations without any choice. Fortunately, there are many agencies dedicated to supporting people in desperate situations. Well designed and made products can help people survive many dangers, and help those who rescue or assist them.

Your challenge is to identify, research and analyse a survival situation, then to design and make a product that will help people to survive or support anyone helping them.

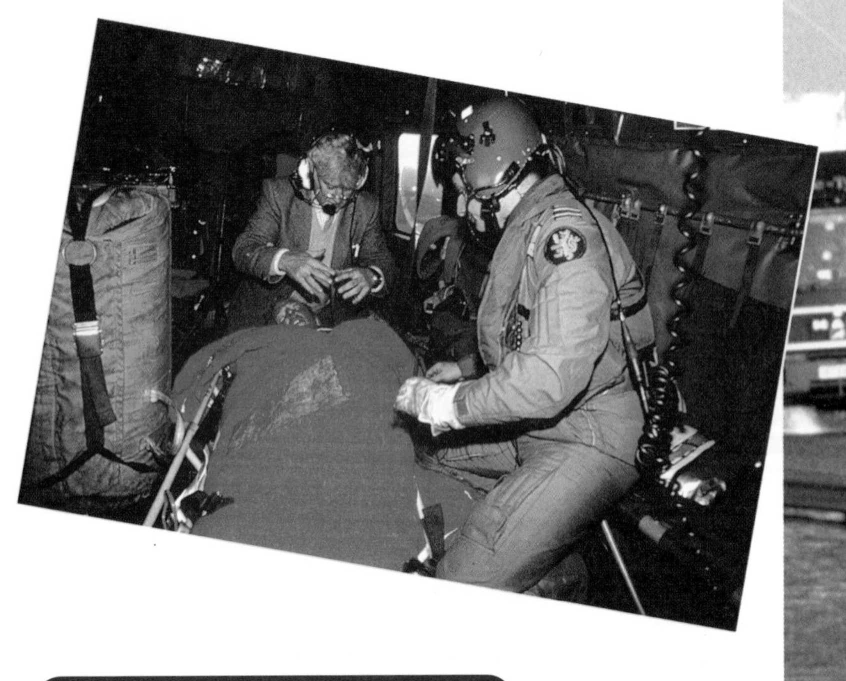

Why this activity is useful

You will have an opportunity to design and make a product that is of great value to the people who will use it. In doing this you will learn to research and understand user needs and constraints in a real way. Someone's life may depend on the product.

You might be able to have your product evaluated in use by experts and may be able to patent your product's design.

You may want to give the idea to an aid agency or emergency service.

Values issues

This DMA gives you a special opportunity to think more about values. Because surviving often depends on others besides the survivor, it may help you to think about these other points of view as well. In particular:

- Should people pay for their rescue if they put themselves in potentially dangerous situations, and then need help?
- Should all people be treated in the same way?
- How should rescue services be funded?
- What do you think about situations where people are starving to death but foreign aid is rejected by their governments?
- Should poor countries have to buy essential products when wealthy nations throw the same things away?
- Should there be an international force to respond to natural disasters?

To be successful

The real success for you will be the satisfaction of designing and making a product to help another person in some way, possibly by saving his or her life.

- Choose a risk situation that you can deal with in school even if it needs outside collaboration.
- Be clear about the amount of risk and the level of trust that will be needed in your product. Avoid situations where the risk or trust involved may turn out to be too great.
- This will be a piece of your assessed coursework. You can increase your chances of exam success by being clear about what the marking scheme expects from you.

How to get going

The first requirement of this assignment requires some lateral thinking – thinking around the problem.

- Two categories of survival situation are given in the project brief – what are they?
- Use these categories to list situations where survival is at stake.
- Carefully analyse some of these situations for the risks involved, and identify potential products that may reduce these risks. (NB Your syllabus might restrict the type of product that is suitable.)
- Do you have any survival experiences to relate your work to?
- Can you get close to a real experience of other survival situations which you have identified?
- Can you talk to people with experience of real survival situations?

BEWARE – You will probably need to visit people and places, take photographs, write letters and wait for replies. All of this is time consuming and needs to be included in your planning.

Leftover food

Your challenge

Vegetable peelings, bread crusts, and pastry offcuts are all examples of ingredients which may be left over from the **production process**. A food manufacturer does not like to waste expensive ingredients and needs to minimise the amounts thrown away. What can a food manufacturer do with these left over ingredients? Greenhalgh's Bakery have bread crusts left over from their sandwich production line which they then use to make a stuffing mix. Pennine Foods have over-ripe avocados which are not suitable for their sandwiches but which are perfect for guacamole dip.

Your challenge is to choose a popular manufactured product and identify possible leftovers from the preparation of ingredients. Design and make a **profitable** and **useful** second product line using these leftover ingredients.

Why this activity is useful

You will become aware of how to avoid waste and make product lines more profitable.

You will be inventive, thinking up new uses for food ingredients.

Your product must be of high quality and meet stringent health and safety regulations. This may be more difficult because you will have to be careful which leftover ingredients you select. What will be safe to use? Choose how you process them by thinking about how the ingredients behave, and make sure the standard of the final product meets people's expectations of quality.

Values issues

You only have to look at the bins in areas where food is served to see that a large amount of food is thrown away everyday. Waste food can be cooked food which is not eaten or raw ingredients which are not used.

- Find out how much waste food your family or school throws away.
- What are the reasons that the food is thrown away?
- How much does this waste food cost?
- Are there systems that school canteens or food manufacturers can use to minimise waste food? Can you make some suggestions to your school canteen?

To be successful

- State which leftover ingredients or components you will be working with.
- Be clear that using this leftover food for a second product line will be cost effective and sensible.
- Design a product of high quality, despite the fact that it uses some ingredients which are leftover from another product.
- Be inventive.
- Carry out health and safety checks on the ingredients you choose, the processing and handling of the ingredients and the production of the final item.
- Try a number of recipes, recording suggestions about each one, in order to refine and improve your idea.

How to get going

- What ingredients are you going to work with? Ask a local food manufacturer to suggest leftovers they have from their production lines. Alternatively, you could watch a video of food manufacturing to give you ideas, or use product disassembly to find out what might be leftover when a particular product is made.
- Pay attention to health and safety regulations. Not all leftover ingredients can be used again. Some foods do not keep well and have a very limited shelf life. You cannot use these, because they might pose a health risk due to microbial growth, or they might not be acceptable to the consumer because of their appearance or texture.
- After you have chosen your ingredient anything is possible, so be inventive. But remember you are helping to make a profitable second product line, so keep an eye on costs and price.

Pre-manufactured components

Your challenge

Many food manufacturers buy **pre-manufactured** components to save time and money in preparation and to ensure each product is the same each time. For example, buying pre-manufactured pureed tomatoes, pastry cases, cake decorations or pizza bases, cuts down on some of the preparation needed.

Your challenge is to design and make a product range making use of a pre-manufactured component.

Why this activity is useful

You will need to identify a suitable pre-manufactured component to use.

You must think about a range of several products which use the same component.

You will have to consider how the pre-manufactured component may be combined/used with fresh foods.

You must identify ways in which quality control is assured.

You must consider if the component you have chosen will make production quicker and cheaper.

Values issues

- Pre-manufactured components are available to use in domestic cooking as well as in industrial manufacturing. You can buy ready-prepared pastry, ready peeled and cut vegetables, ready-made flan cases, ready-made meringue nests, etc. In the past there were few pre-manufactured components to help in the preparation of products. Can you suggest why the number has increased?
- What types of people do you think buy ready-prepared components and why?
- To a manufacturer, what are the advantages and disadvantages of using pre-manufactured components instead of custom-made parts when designing and making?

To be successful

- Carry out research to find out the types of pre-manufactured components available.
- Choose a component which allows you to design a distinct and new product range.
- Experiment with different ideas for the products.
- Think about all the health and safety controls necessary for safe production of the products.
- Consider how the pre-manufactured component will speed up production of the products and make them cheaper.

How to get going

- Firstly consider the pre-manufactured components available. Choose a component which allows you to make a range of different but similar products.
- Carry out comparative tests to choose the best type or brand to use. For example, set up a test to see how different ready-made pizza bases measure up to your needs. Consider cost, storage time, consumer acceptability and ease of use.
- Carry out sensory evaluation of your products before deciding on the final recipes.
- Modify and improve your recipes to meet the product range specification.
- Build in procedures to ensure each product is made to the same high quality.

Bottling it up

Your challenge

Exotic chutneys, jams and conserves, fruit vinegars, brandied fruits, herbs in oil, sauces and marinades are just some examples of the range of foods now available in jars and bottles. Extending the **shelf life** of foods has been an important part of food technology over the centuries. Manufacturers have always sought to improve the **quality** of the finished product, but the principles have remained the same.

Your challenge is to manufacture a preserve in a glass container. For the development of this product, you will have to determine the specification for the raw materials, taking into consideration the quality of the finished product.

Why this activity is useful

Companies specify to producers the exact qualities they require from an ingredient for a particular product, so you will investigate the variety and range of each ingredient and understand how their properties and qualities affect the final outcome.

You will have a greater understanding of the principles involved in preserving food, and utilise them in your own prototype to achieve the product you desire.

You will be more aware of the source and production of raw food materials.

Values issues

- Traditional and modern methods of biotechnology have been used to preserve food through the ages. Discuss how you feel about food being modified in this way.
- The diversity of many foods is diminishing rapidly due to the requirements of food manufacturers. The choice for the shopper can be limited. How do you see this affecting food in the future?

To be successful

You will:

- ★ Investigate how different foods can be preserved and demonstrate your understanding of the effects of different types of preservation on foods.
- ★ Test your product using different varieties and food processing methods, recording the differences, and use this information to produce a higher quality product.
- ★ Identify the qualities demanded by your target market and draw up a specification for each ingredient to meet these.
- ★ Produce a prototype that is successfully preserved and indicate how it would be made on a larger scale.

How to get going

- Decide on the type of preserve that you are going to develop, e.g. sauce, chutney. You will need a basic recipe.
- Identify which ingredients a food manufacturer could vary and which ones you will investigate. Determine which varieties are available and how they will be processed. Draw up a production plan.
- Allow time to conduct sensory analysis tests for each batch.
- Consider time, quantities, temperature and containers.

Corn around the World

Your challenge

Technology has been an important factor in expanding the range of products made from one basic food. **Staple foods** are being given a new lease of life and have become a fashionable food in their "new" form. Rice and bread are still old favourites and, like corn, they are continually being developed to cater for current trends in both health and eating habits. Crops became staple foods because they can be grown easily in a particular country, many have now become global foods because of improved transportation and the advances in food processing.

Your challenge is to choose a basic food and investigate the forms in which it is available.

You have been asked to find a novel way of using this food and develop a new food product which will appeal to a particular **target group**.

Why this activity is useful

You will gain a wider knowledge of how a basic ingredient can have a variety of roles, which are dependent upon how it is processed and developed.

You may also achieve a better understanding of the economic and political influences behind food production.

You will be able to justify the commercial worth of a product.

You will understand how manufacturers use and need a specification about the raw material they obtain.

Values issues

- Governments in many countries encourage certain crops to be grown. Subsidies can result in excess amounts being produced and often goods are made solely for export. What do you feel about current policies regarding the production and supply of food?
- Organic produce is now widely available. List some advantages of organic products. What problems do the producers of these commodities face?
- A huge range of imported fruit and vegetables is now used. This demand for "exotic" food by western countries has provided a valuable source of income to the supplying countries. Look at some food labels to see which countries of origin are stated. How do you think these new business enterprises have changed the lifestyles of the local population?

To be successful

You will:

- Research a selection of staple foods and investigate one in detail.
- Become familiar with the various forms in which the food is available and be able to suggest new ways of using it.
- Experiment with different ideas and different varieties of the staple food.
- Produce a prototype with a detailed specification and the unit operations for your product.

How to get going

- Compile a list of staple foods that are available and identify the one you would like to investigate. Explore the different forms in which it is already available. Don't forget to look at more unusual staple foods such as millet and quinoa.
- What considerations have influenced its development? (These may be political, economic, historical, social or scientific.)
- Evaluate how consumers make use of foods and how strong their desire for a new food product is. Identify the market sector for your product.
- Allow time to experiment with novel ways of using the food.
- Produce a flow diagram outlining unit operations for the production of your product.

Off the shelf

Your challenge

Britons spend more than £1 million every day on **chilled meals**. However, not everyone may like the foods that manufacturers combine into products for them. To get around this problem, some supermarkets allow consumers to make their own choices, e.g. you will find pick-and-mix **pizza** bars in some supermarkets.

Imagine a selling point (in a supermarket) offering **prepared products**, which consumers may pick and combine to make their own meal or dish. Your challenge (as a food manufacturer) is to design and make a **selection** of products which would fulfil this need.

Why this activity is useful

You will develop individual parts of a meal or product, which consumers may choose to combine in different ways.

You will put into practice what you know about shelf life qualities and health and safety regulations in relation to the display of each component.

You will learn how the different portions and sizes can be paid for.

Your research skills will be put to the test, as the components must appeal to a wide range of consumers.

Values issues

- ◆ A few years ago, a product such as a "baked bean pizza" would have been unheard of. Can you explain why manufacturers started to try out different and unusual ideas?
- ◆ How can you encourage consumers to eat more healthily?
- ◆ What packaging materials will be used and how can these be minimised without risk to health?
- ◆ How will you ensure your products appeal to different groups?
- ◆ Additives could be used to prolong the shelf life of your product; which ones would you use and why?
- ◆ How can you make sure that customers with food allergies are not endangered by your products?

To be successful

You will:

- ★ Look at different products to identify their component parts.
- ★ Look at and research into a product that will be popular.
- ★ Think carefully about the type of product you want consumers to put together.
- ★ Ensure people do not take too much of the most expensive component, so there is no profit.
- ★ Check that each component you produce is interesting and will be bought.
- ★ Consider how visually attractive the components are.
- ★ Consider how the complete meal will be carried home and cooked or reheated safely.

How to get going

- Look carefully at popular dishes to identify the components used.
- Research what people like and dislike about existing products.
- Consider how you will encourage consumers to try out ideas and tastes which are new to them.
- How many of the components will customers be able to put together?
- Remember to include instructions for reheating the product safely.
- Will all the different components be put in one package or container to carry home? What are the health and safety risks?

DESIGNING

Where do new design ideas for food products come from?

The majority of new ideas come from product development teams who work for large food companies. In smaller companies this may be the responsibility of just one individual.

Product development is all about ideas – imaginative, creative, sensible, or even wacky, ideas – that put food ingredients together in new and interesting ways. Often this involves ingredients which have not been associated with each other before. Out of a hundred ideas, perhaps only ten will be made up as samples and many of these will fail and be dropped.

New products can have a major impact on our lives: we live in fast-changing times! Conversely, it can be a change in lifestyle that brings opportunity for new food products.

New ideas come from:

- brainstorming by new product development teams in food companies
- keeping track of competitors' new products globally
- competitions in magazines
- inventors (who sell ideas)
- customer complaints
- specialist consultants
- new recipe books
- recipes from famous restaurants and their chefs
- fashion trends (food can be like clothes and shoes)
- growth in overseas travel bringing knowledge and experience of ethnic foods
- health trends and government guidelines.

How do you turn an idea or a recipe into a commercial product that can be manufactured in quantity?

It's simple, really! But you need to have a systematic approach. It will probably not be cost effective to reproduce a product in exactly the same way as you do in a test kitchen, restaurant or at home. There are usually too many different stages in the recipe or too many ingredients.

Stop and think

The following questions need to be considered:

- What are the key characteristics of the product that you wish to retain?
- What ingredients could be left out without losing these characteristics?
- How can the recipe be simplified to reflect manufacturing constraints?
- Are there any ingredients available to manufacturers that could be beneficial?

Let's take an example of a potato-topped meat pie. A development team was asked to come up with ideas for a traditional hot pie for the chilled ready-meal market. The development team came up with a **Christmas roast dinner pie**: all the ingredients of this traditional meal layered in one dish.

The recipe included:

- layers of roast turkey
- sliced boiled ham
- whole cooked chipolatas
- whole boiled carrots
- whole boiled sprouts
- stuffing balls
- gravy
- small roast potatoes

Delicious, but far too complicated for even an initial factory trial!

Here is how the product was simplified during the factory trial:

- roast turkey (breast and dark meat)
- sliced cooked chipolatas
- sliced steamed carrots
- gravy
- piped mashed potato

This combination is less labour intensive, with shorter cooking times, and therefore it is cheaper to manufacture in large amounts.

Focused task

Find a recipe that you think would make an interesting product. Using all the information you can find about manufacturing this food product, decide how you could successfully make it on a commercial basis in large quantities.

Concept development

What is concept development?

A concept is a general notion about a food product, around which ideas can be developed. It is a starting point for further development work.

The concept development stage involves modelling and developing the concept to a final product (putting ideas into practice and thinking them through with real materials). A specification can then be drawn up which helps people who will be working on its further development to visualise (**conceptualise**) the product they are to develop. It also gives them something objective to evaluate against, during the prototype and trialling stages.

A concept may be generated:

- to meet a particular need
- to satisfy a new area of the market
- to create a product that fits into a particular price band
- for a particular food commodity and ingredient
- to take advantage of a new way of eating or combining particular foods
- to improve or update an old product.

Drinks like Tango, Lucozade and Irn Bru have been re-styled to make them more appealing to young people

Concept development

Focused task: **Concepts**

One way of thinking about concepts is to see them as hooks on which ideas can be hung and then developed. Here are some examples.

Designing with nutrition in mind, e.g. low fat products

Designing for a particular time of day, e.g. breakfast foods

Designing for a particular time of year, e.g. making use of seasonal foods

Add some of your own examples for each category, or add your own categories and examples.

Focused task: **Generating ideas**

As you know ideas do not often come out of nowhere, although there may be the occasional "eureka" moment or flash of inspiration which leads to a quite different and successful product. Most of the time we have to work hard to develop our ideas. The following techniques can help you:

- Ask questions about what the product will be like and who will eat it.
- Look at what competitors are doing in the same area.
- Evaluate a range of existing and similar products.
- Look through recipe books at some of the established tried and tested ideas, and those from other times and cultures.
- Create mood or image boards to provide a visual image which communicates the concept being developed.
- Use brainstorming.
- Use attribute analysis, i.e. considering the attributes or characteristics such as texture, key flavours and appearance. These may be produced as a star diagram.
- Use market research.

Concept screening

Case study: Concept screening using the innovation funnel

At Birds Eye Wall's the "innovation funnel" model is used to generate, develop and evaluate concepts. A simplified version of the funnel is shown in the diagram below. This is a way of concept screening or testing the feasibility of the concept. The process begins with marketing and product development people brainstorming ideas. The ideas are filtered (or screened) through a number of stages, which become fewer and more focused as they progress. They are tested to see if they are realistic. Eventually, the best ideas are narrowed down to the one that seems most worthwhile developing, and this is put forward for development.

Stop and think

When you have a range of ideas for your designing and making assignment, use the "innovation funnel" to help you narrow them down until you reach the best idea.

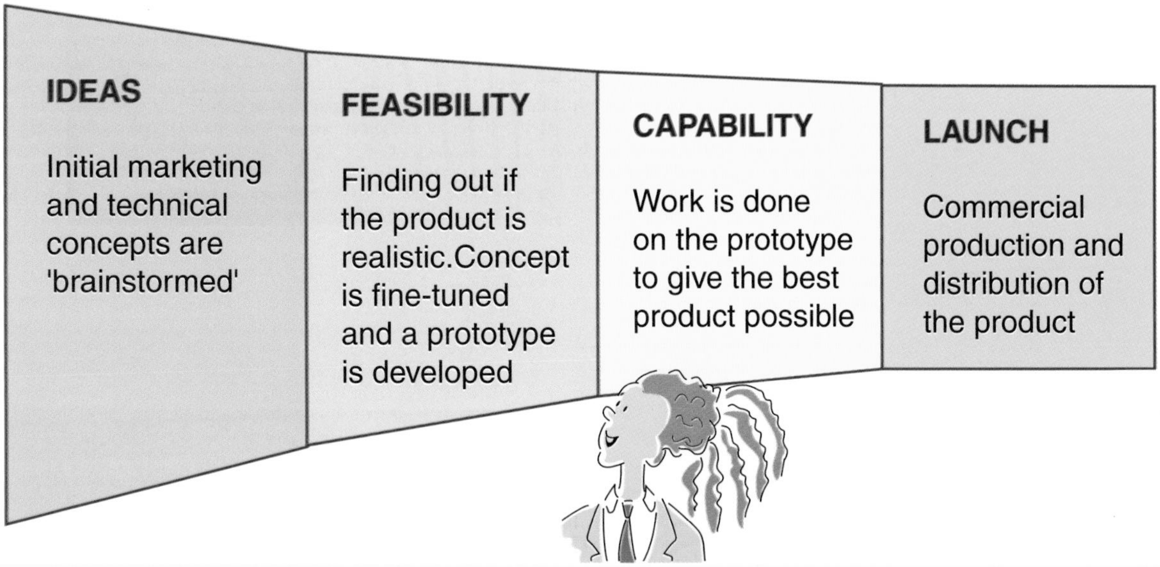

IDEAS

Initial marketing and technical concepts are 'brainstormed'

FEASIBILITY

Finding out if the product is realistic.Concept is fine-tuned and a prototype is developed

CAPABILITY

Work is done on the prototype to give the best product possible

LAUNCH

Commercial production and distribution of the product

Becoming a food detective!

To work successfully in product design and development you must know what's new on the supermarket shelf. The product development team buys and tastes competitors' products. This is often referred to as **market intelligence**.

How can you research the market you are interested in infiltrating? Try the following:

- Watch the market to see what other manufacturers are doing. What are the new products on the market? What are the general trends, e.g. toddler drinks?
- Go out and about. Go to shops to find out about all the products on the market which are similar to yours. Go to food exhibitions, trade fairs and check out new restaurant menus.
- Watch television, to see what new products are being advertised or launched.
- Read food magazines. Look up information from trade journals, e.g. *Grocer* on CD-ROM. Watch out for adverts in magazines, newspapers, billboards.

Concept screening

Case study: Toasties from Findus

Findus have combined one of Britain's simplest pieces of cooking equipment, the toaster, with the nation's taste for the popular pizza. Toasties comprise a light lattice pastry with pizza style filling – launch flavours are Ham and Cheese, Cheese and Tomato, and Bolognese. Development work ensured that the fillings do not seep into the toaster. The concept was seen as perfect for the snack market, both in terms of flavour and speed of cooking. The product is already available in the UK, Italy and Germany and is being tested in Southern Spain, Portugal, the Benelux and Nordic countries. Findus is active in developing the range further and is looking to develop the whole hand-held food sector.

Focused task: Design a new scone

Develop a new scone for an in-store supermarket bakery. The new scone will be produced daily and sold in packs of four. It should offer something novel and imaginative to supplement the existing range.

Here are some ideas to help you begin your detective work:

- What types of scone are in the existing range?
- Who else (apart from supermarkets) sells scones? What sort of scones are they selling?
- How many different types are there?
- What is the selling price (from cheapest to most expensive)?
- Use a spreadsheet to compare cost per 100g of product.
- How many different user groups are there? What are their preferences, e.g. economy family packs, luxury all butter, organic whole-wheat, hand-baked?

The results from this research will be fundamental to the success of your project:

- You will know what is already being sold, so you can develop something new.
- Other people's ideas can be a major source of inspiration, however good or bad they are.
- You will be able to identify gaps in the market and seize the opportunity to fill one of them.

Thinking about people's values

Food products are right at the heart of the differences between people as individuals, as nationalities and as cultures. For this reason, a great deal of care must be taken to consider individual, national and cultural differences when you are developing new food products.

D&T Routes Core Book page 37

Focused task: Role play

The following activity is called a **simulation**. This means that you will be acting out (simulating) a real situation, so you can experience it for yourself.

Work in groups of about five. Each person in the group will take one of the roles below:

- An environmental expert (interested in organic food)
- An expert on different cultures and traditions
- A food technologist (expert on traditional tastes) who developed the new idea
- A financial expert (also the chairperson)
- A timekeeper and minutes taker.

Step 1: Read about the situation.

Step 2: Carry out research into your role. Find out what the key issues might be for your character in this scenario and what different points of view exist.

Prepare your own opinions and have the evidence ready. Remember you must stay "in role" and only represent the character's point of view.

Step 3: Hold a meeting of your group. Remember that you are playing a role. Allow each person a few minutes to put forward their opinions. Each person must be allowed the same amount of time. Debate all the issues thoroughly and decide if your company should start manufacturing this new product range.

Step 4: Prepare a group report explaining your decisions and listing your recommendations for changes and improvements.

Reflection

- What have you learnt about values issues from this simulation?
- Have you considered a new point of view?
- Have you changed your opinions?

Scenario

You are the group that decides if new product lines should be manufactured for a large "ethical" company. The product under discussion today has been developed by the food technologists. It is a new variety of luxury individual pie. The pie is like a samosa and is made from filo pastry. It will be square and have a range of filling choices:

Asparagus and ham	Salmon and prawn
Chicken curry	Tongue and mushroom

They would be sold as chilled food. Sources of the raw foods have been found in this country when possible and also imported from Africa and South America.

Developing a specification

Food companies develop new products from an initial brief and then use market research and concept modelling to put together an outline specification. This is similar to the process you follow at school.

As the product is modified and refined, the specification becomes more precise. The final product will have a detailed specification that contains the finished product standards for the materials, processes, shelf life and packaging. These will be agreed by the manufacturer and the retailer.

There may be a separate marketing specification too.

D&T Routes Core Book page 51

Focused task: *Writing your outline specification*

Begin with a description of the product stating its function or purpose, use the following headings to help you:

- aesthetics
- costs
- ingredients
- health and safety
- environmental issues
- shelf life
- product life.

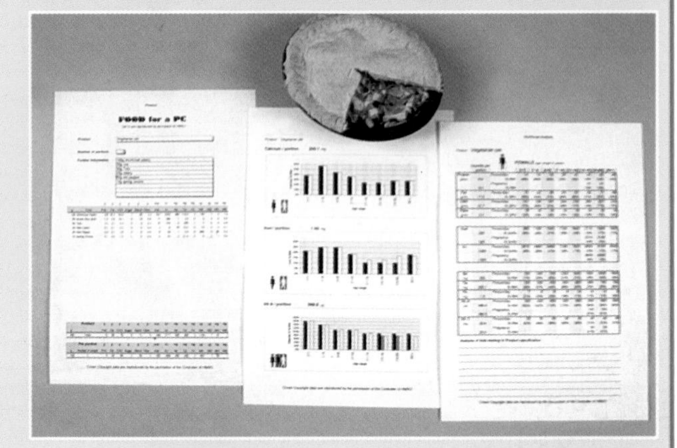

The Gap in the Market! As far as I know there is no other sandwich on the market like this range. I have seen that more and more people want to solve their illnesses and pains without using drugs, that is why I think now is the time to introduce this new range, I also think that there will be other products like mine coming out soon.

Unique Selling Point This sandwich stands out from all the other sandwiches because of the fact that it will help cure illnesses. I hope to make it the same sort of price as all the others, but because it is different and will look good my product will stand out from all the other sandwiches.

Consumer I hope that my sandwich will appeal to all age, but I am mainly aiming it at people who are working, which is anyone from 16 to 50, but to be more specific I hope that middle age people buy this sandwich. I think that women will take an interest in this sandwich. I hope this sandwich will be priced so every social class will be interested.

Sandwiches

I am going to make a new range of sandwiches which help to cure illnesses like headaches with natural herbs.

Situations I am aiming this sandwich to be sold in sandwich bars, Bakers, supermarkets, staff canteens, and Garage forecourts, so it will be eaten out of the house at lunch time. Because this is a main food I would expect it to be eaten with a bit of fruit or a yogurt or some sort of fruit dessert and a fruit juice, or it could be eaten with a packet of crisps or a chocolate bar, even a slice of cake!

Cost I really want this sandwich to be as cheap as possible, but to be very good quality, so I think it will cost about as much as other sandwiches, which on average is about £1.40 for an average sized sandwich.

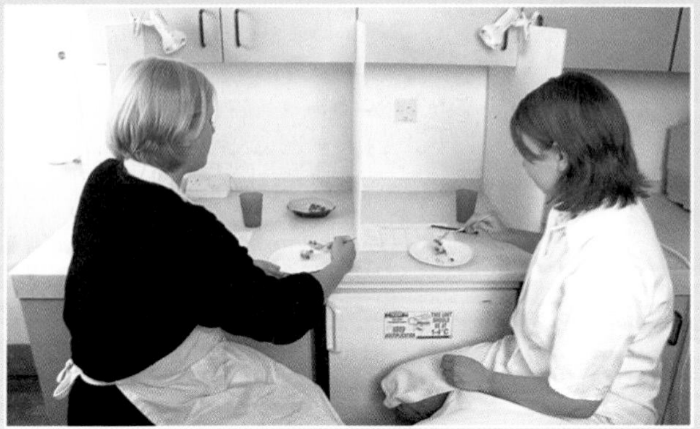

Working towards a more detailed specification

During this phase of your designing, you will continually refine the outline specification until you are in a position to agree the finished product standards.

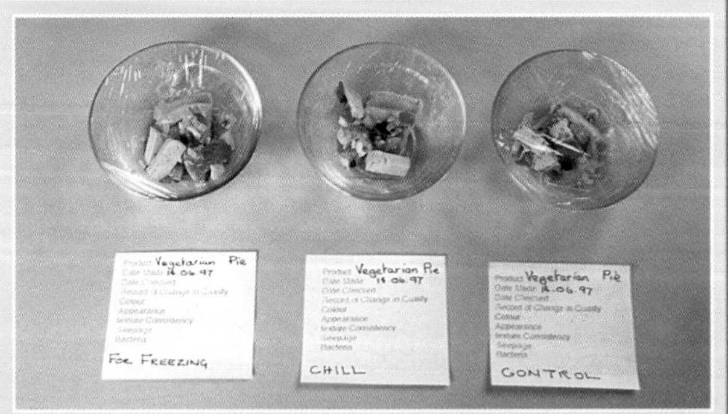

There are a number of activities that you will have to carry out during this phase before you can agree a more precise specification. What are they?

The food industry demands that health, safety and hygiene are taken very seriously as part of the product development process, partly because British and International law demands it and also because it is fundamental to a successful product–customer relationship. For this reason, retailers and manufacturers usually keep a folder containing information about each product they make or sell. This is highly confidential.

PASTR

Appearance	Shortcrust made with maize and wheat flour, vegeta shortening and egg yolk, slightly yellow glow with a ma surface, smooth and golden
Aroma	A savoury biscuit overlay with notes of wheat
Flavour	Delicate and subtle with notes of butyric acid and sodium
Mouthfeel	Crisp to initial bite then little resistance and melt away without cloying

WHITE SAUCE

Appearance	Smooth sauce with flecks of tarragon (5 pieces per 25 cubic cm), no discolouration or lumps of starch
Aroma	Clean with weak tarragon and roast chicken notes
Flavour	Dominant roast chicken with clean milk flavour and tarragon
Mouthfeel	Thick and creamy but smooth and non-cloying

CHICKEN

Appearance	White clean breast meat (no discolouration), without skin, at 25x25 mm rough dice
Aroma	Clean, fresh, roast chicken
Flavour	Fresh tasting with no off notes
Mouthfe	Tender and moist with no detectabl ryness

In industry, the manufacturing specification is a formal contract between the manufacturer and the retailer, agreeing the exact details about the product. It contains precise information that can be used to measure and ensure consistent quality. It can be referred to if there are any problems or complaints about the quality of the materials, processes, shelf life and packaging during the product's life. Once signed, any changes have to be agreed by all parties.

Focused task: Working towards a manufacturing specification

The headings below are used by a large food company. Use them to help you build up the finished product standard for your own product:

Name of product

Finished Product Standards

description of product
detailed ingredients
weight/size
number of units together
product life
distribution and display requirements
quality standards — visually; taste panel
microbiological standards
analytical standards — nutritional information; calorific analysis

Processing standards

recipe
HACCP flowchart
Safety Critical Control Points
Quality Critical Control Points
Legal requirements

Modelling and communicating with IT

IT can be used to support food product design and development:

- In designing, we can make good use of computers to model ideas: what a product will look like, the costs involved and its nutritional value.
- We use computers to communicate our ideas to others during the development process.
- IT is also valuable in communicating with consumers and retailers once a product has been developed.
- Sometimes, as the case study shows, IT can be used to predict how consumers will respond to a product when it is displayed in shops.

Case study: *Virtual supermarket*

At Birds Eye Walls, a virtual reality modelling system is used by marketing specialists. This helps them to model how food products will look on a supermarket shelf. The effect of displaying products on different shelves at different heights and angles can be tried and tested without going to the shop itself. The impact on the consumer can then be predicted.

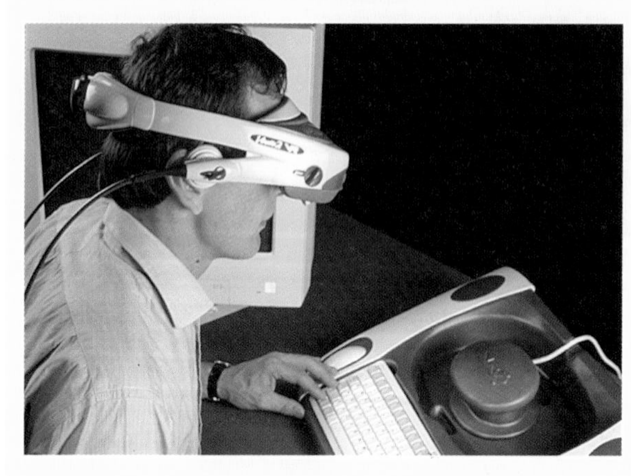

Computer modelling can be used successfully to:

- Predict the effect of combining certain ingredients, to work out costs, or to carry out nutritional analysis
- Model the overall effect on the food product
- Present data as graphs and charts.

This helps food technologists to make decisions about what quantities and which components to use and it helps the marketing people decide what the product should cost.

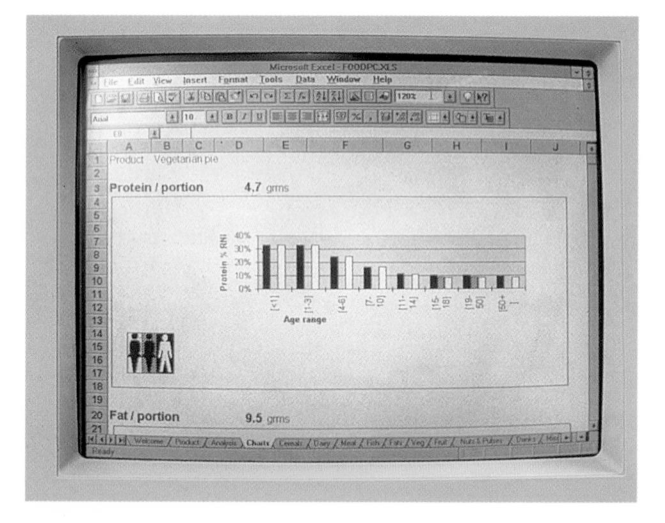

Focused task: Using IT

Take a basic recipe for fruit pie and model the effects of changing the fruit filling on the costs. You might try changing:

- the type of fruit
- the mixture of fruits
- the proportion of fruit to other ingredients
- the total quantity of fruit.

When you have two or three formulae that are worth developing, produce a prototype of each. Evaluate them for acceptability in terms of flavour, appearance and cost.

Computers are used to design packaging and to select and test suitable packaging materials. Packaging graphics should communicate their messages clearly. Different colours and graphic effects can be modelled and tried out, and the best ones chosen. This is less time-consuming than drawing out by hand. Software can be used to design nets. The image can then be transferred immediately onto the packaging for printing.

Evaluating food products

Evaluation is part of the development process which shapes and refines the end product. As a product is modelled, tested and trialled, it is constantly adapted and improved. This is partly by trial-and-error, although it is carried out by technical experts who have a real knowledge and expertise about how food materials behave and react to conditions. They have a range of evaluation tools and techniques available. These include: sensory analysis, product disassembly and nutritional analysis.

The end product is usually the result of ideas which have been modified, improved, combined and refined over time. This is often quite different from the first idea the development team started with.

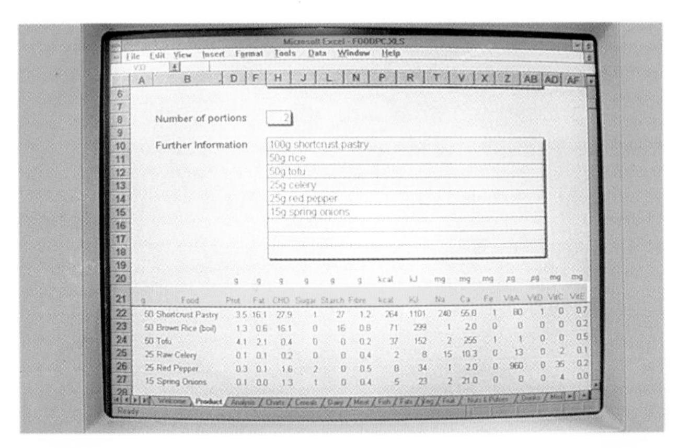

Aesthetics play an important role in our choice and enjoyment of food. Aesthetics describe the way we respond to food with our senses: sight, hearing, touch, taste and smell.

D&T Routes Core Book
page 68

We expect food to give us pleasant sensations

How many times have you refused to eat something because you did not like the look of it? Ask your friends to name a food product they dislike. Ask them why and they will probably point out reasons to do with the texture, taste and colour of the food. Any testing which relies on people's likes and dislikes is known as **subjective**, because it varies from person to person.

Evaluating aesthetic appeal is very important. Food designers carry out a number of different types of test during the planning and making of products. These can be consumer preference tests or sensory analysis.

Sensory analysis

Taste panels are an important evaluation technique.

Subjective tests

Subjective tests such as **preference tests** indicate how much a product is liked or disliked. They are useful when assessing product acceptability and manufacturers may use them to evaluate their product against their competitors' products. Food and packaging can be discussed by a consumer panel. This involves people discussing how they feel about a product during the prototype stage. It relies on people's feelings, and so gives the designer a good idea of how the product will be received by the public.

Correlations between attributes and preference dimensions for unpeeled apples

Cooking apple (ie)
Granny Smith
UNRIPE
Crisp (t)
ACIDIC
Fresh (ff)
Grassy (ff)
HARD
Juicy (ea)
GREEN APPLE
Tough skin (fb)
White specs (ea)
Empire
Jonagold
Falstaff
Royal Gala
Skin bits (t)
White (ia)
Shiny (ea)
Braeburn
PLUM/CHERRY
Watery (ff)
BITTER
Dark specs (ea)
Fiesta
White dust (ea)
Golden Delicious
Gala
Cox
YELLOW
Cox-like (ff)
Red Delicious
Ridges (ea)
MUSTY
RED APPLE
Spartan
Brown (ea)
Soapy (ff)
Red streaks (ea)
Peardrops (ff)
Off flavour
SWEET

Dimension 2 (14.8 %)

Dimension 1 (24.5 %)

ifr

Information gathered from sensory analysis can be used to chart people's preferences against the attributes of a particular product. This chart maps people's preferences for apples against the types of different apples available. By finding out what most people like, a good manufacturer is then able to choose the ingredients and develop the final product to match consumer taste.

Objective tests

Objective tests are also needed. Descriptive tests measure consumer response to particular characteristics of food products:

- **Scoring tests** Taste testers are asked to make judgements about the quality of certain product characteristics. They are usually asked to rank on a scale, for example, how sweet they find a product from very sweet to not at all sweet.
- **Ranking tests** Several different samples are presented and tasters are asked to rank them in order of preference in relation to a specific characteristic, e.g. a texture such as crispness.
- **Discrimination tests** Samples are compared to find out whether any differences are detectable between them.

Scoring tests

Ranking tests

Small amounts of recipes may be made up as samples. Each of these samples are made to slightly different recipes, so that the results can be tested and compared for preference and against the specification.

- **Paired comparison tests** Two samples are presented and the taster is asked whether they can detect a specific difference, e.g. which of the products is sweeter.
- **Triangle tests** Three samples are presented, two of which are identical and the taster is asked to identify the "odd one out".
- **Duo–trio tests** Out of three samples, tasters are told which is the control and asked which of the other two samples differs from the control.

Duo–trio tests

Paired comparison tests

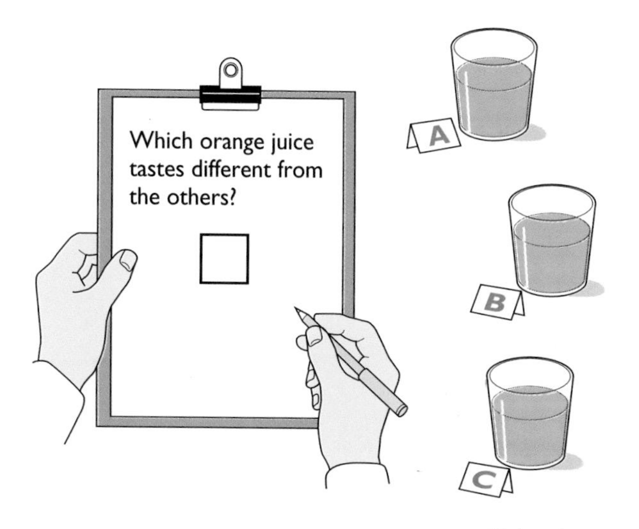

Triangle tests

Star profiles are drawn up to help analyse and describe the attributes of the product and to then test and evaluate against these criteria. Star profiles may also be created on a computer spreadsheet.

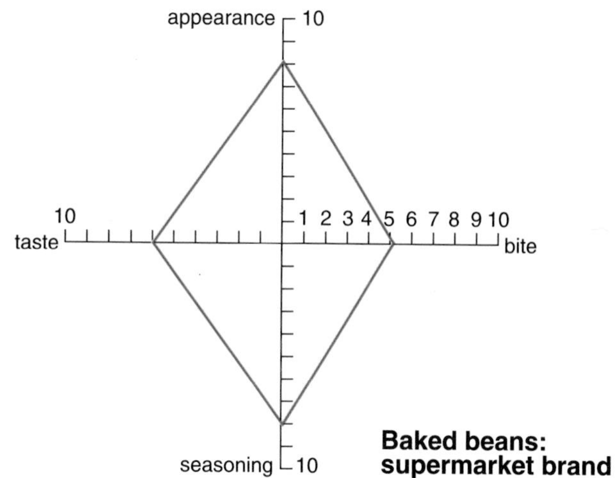

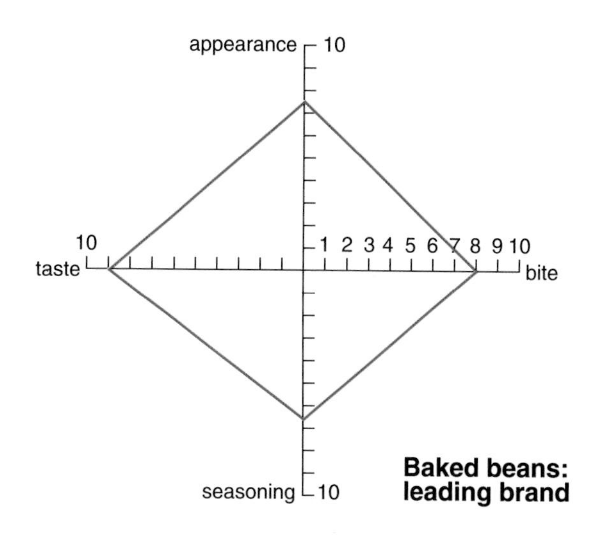

DESIGNING

Sensory analysis

Case study: Quantified texture analysis

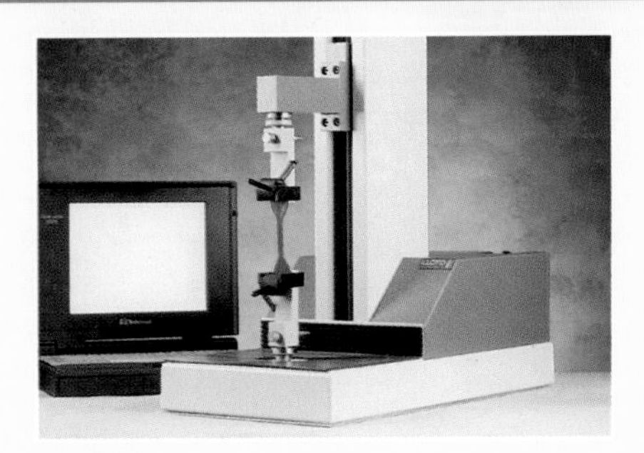

Texture analysis is used by the food industry as an objective measure of texture. It can be used to test spreadability, gumminess, springiness, hardness, snap strength, cohesiveness, chewiness, stickiness, elasticity, extrusion force, crispness.

- What do you think each of these terms mean?
- What kind of product might be tested for each one?

Texture analysis is used to help research, develop ideas, evaluate production and process control.

Disassembly

Existing food products are often analysed during product development to help stimulate ideas. The food technologist is likely to analyse the existing product by **disassembly**. The food technologist may be briefed to produce an identical product, an economy version or an improved version of the product. By analysing its component ingredients and the processes which have been used to produce and assemble it, they can develop a specification for their own version, using the competitor's product as a benchmark against which to make comparisons. They will be analysing it to see:

- what makes the product successful
- where it could be improved
- any opportunities which were missed
- how and why different materials and manufacturing processes have been used.

Nutritional analysis

Nutrition may be a consideration during the development of the product, e.g. when creating a product for a special diet. It will be important to test how the product performs nutritionally.

Focused task: Evaluating

1 Select a food product which interests you (or which you are currently working on).

2 Select 3–4 versions of the product, disassemble them and carry out sensory analysis.

Do the right thing!

- When working on your own product refer back to the outline specification and evaluate how well your design fulfils the criteria for the product.
- Does it fulfil the sensory requirements of taste, texture, appearance, aroma?
- Is it within your approximate costing estimate?
- Is it suitable for the lifestyle of your target audience?
- What quality of materials will you choose, and will you use any pre-manufactured components?
- Are there any high-risk health, safety and hygiene implications?
- Where will you sell the product? In what conditions? What will its shelf life be?

Choosing the right food materials

All the materials we use for design come from combinations of just over a hundred elements in the periodic table, food is no exception.

It is amazing, then, that there is such an enormous variety of materials for us to use and develop products from. How can we select the right materials to use?

Choices will be influenced by the following factors:

- type of product, e.g. dairy, meat or cereal-based
- the retail price of the intended product
- the sector of the market the product will be in, e.g. chilled, fresh, frozen, canned, bottled
- the behaviour of fresh food post-harvest or post-slaughter
- the chosen method of processing
- the behaviour of cooked or processed foods that are not to be eaten immediately.

This chart is useful in several ways. It can tell you why a particular ingredient has been included in a product or suggest the group of materials you can use to achieve a desired effect or outcome in a product you are developing.

Functions of materials

Each material in a food product is specially selected to perform a particular function. These functions are identified in the product specification:

sensory function
A food material may be selected because it can give a product a particular colour, flavour, texture or aroma, e.g. glucose syrup provides sweetness.

nutritional function
A food material may be selected because it has a particular nutritional content, e.g. oatflakes provide dietary fibre.

physical function
A food material may be selected because it performs a vital physical function, i.e. it provides the product with a specific structure and texture, e.g. vegetable oil will help to combine and hold together the other ingredients.

Stop and think

Can you identify which material performs the most functions and can you suggest why?

Physical functions

	Food materials												
Working characteristic	Fats	Eggs	Pulses	Cereals	Fruit	Vegetables	Sugar	Meat	Fish	Milk	Flours	Water	Oils
Aerating (lightening)	●	●					●						
Binding	●	●		●							●		
Browning/colour	●	●		●			●			●			●
Emulsifying		●											
Flavouring	●	●	●		●	●	●	●	●	●			●
Moistening	●	●			●	●	●			●			●
Preserving	●						●						●
Setting		●											
Shortening	●												●
Stabilising		●									●		
Sweetening					●		●						
Thickening		●	●	●	●	●					●		
Thinning							●			●		●	

Choosing the right food materials

Focused task: What does each ingredient do?

Look at the ingredients list on a packet of cereal bars or another food product. With a partner, discuss why each ingredient has been used. Compare your answers with those of another pair in your class.

INGREDIENTS
OATFLAKES, GLUCOSE SYRUP, ROASTED PEANUTS, PUFFED RICE, VEGETABLE AND HYDROGENATED VEGETABLE OIL, CHOCOLATE CHIPS, DEXTROSE, ROASTED HAZELNUTS, SUGAR, SWEETENED CONDENSED SKIMMED MILK, BUTTER, ICING SUGAR, GLYCERINE, COCOA POWDER, SALT, EMULSIFIER: LECITHIN.

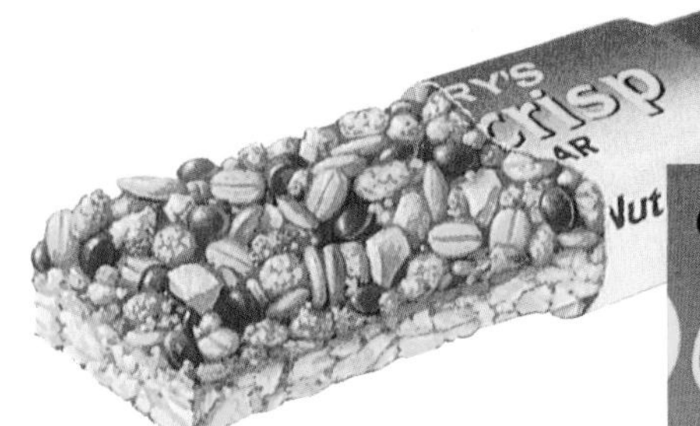

CHOCOLATE CHIP & NUT
Chewy & crisp
CEREAL BARS

Focused task: Biscuit ingredients

Home-made style biscuits have recently enjoyed renewed popularity, mainly because of their wholesome, home-cooked appeal. Using the sample blank chart, model your initial ideas for 3 or 4 'wholesome' recipes.

Food material	Sensory function	Nutritional function	Physical function

Functions and characteristics of food materials

Food materials are complex substances and behave in different ways. A food manufacturer must make use of these different properties in a controlled way, so that products are of a consistent quality. Food scientists and food technologists spend a long time researching how materials behave under different temperature conditions and when other substances are added.

To help you design new food products and make them successful, you will need to know how certain materials react and behave in different conditions. You will need to understand their physical functions and working characteristics.

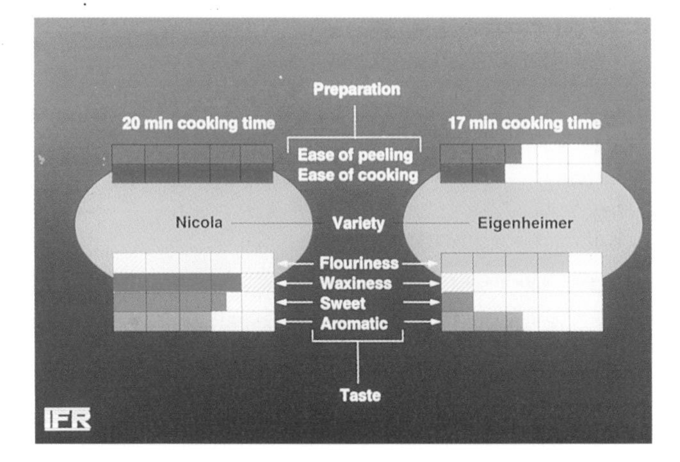

Product developers develop, test and modify prototypes until they find the best conditions and combinations of materials for the product. The specification outlines what the product will look and taste like, the food materials needed to achieve the necessary colour, flavour and texture, and the likely costs involved.

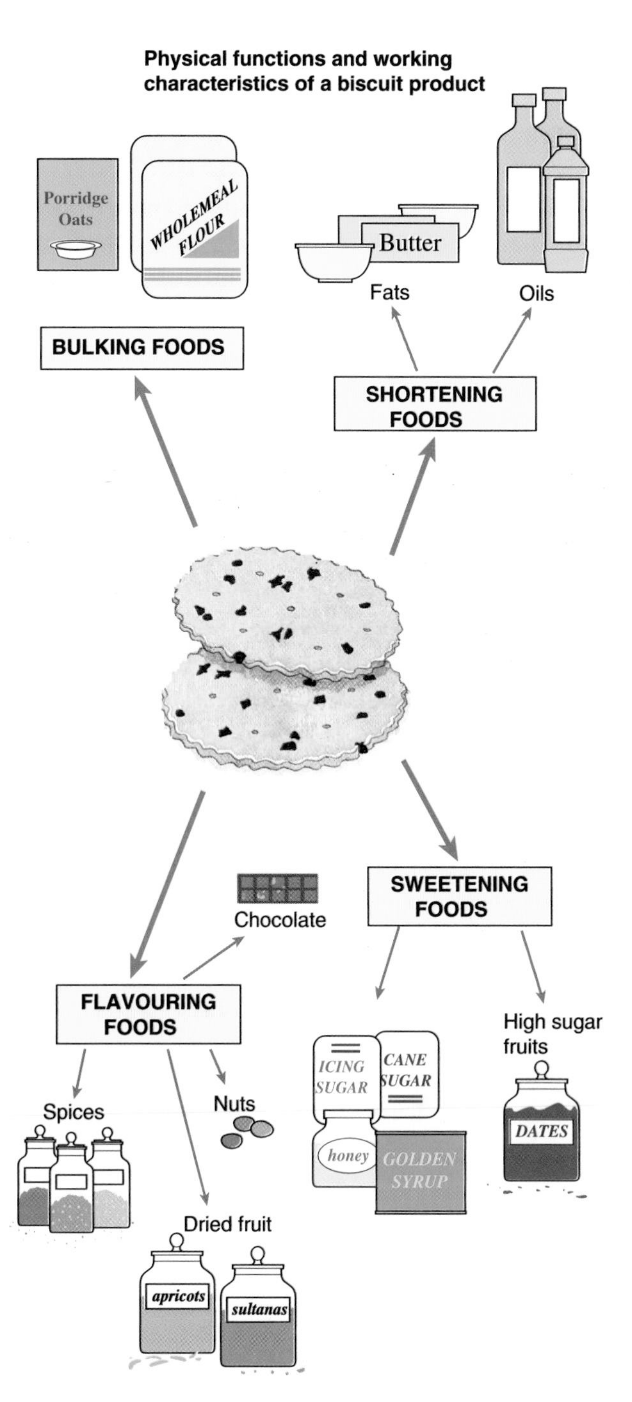

Focused task: Summary chart of functions

To help you understand the physical functions of food materials, they can be grouped by the way in which they work:

thickening aerating moistening sweetening setting binding shortening flavouring stabilising emulsifying thinning preserving

Draw a summary chart of functions and uses such as the one below. Use your own knowledge and the following practical investigations to help you.

Food material	Physical function	Working characteristics	Example products
Protein: Albumin in egg white	Aeration	Foaming when whipped	Pavlova

Practical investigations

The following practical investigations are to do with food chemistry. Each task will help you understand the working characteristics of a particular food or group of foods.

You will need to observe:

1. what changes take place
2. how long it takes before anything happens
3. the temperature at which it occurs
4. whether anything else is needed to make it happen.

You will need to record your results.

Practical investigation 1 – Helping ingredients combine (emulsions)

Manufacturers need to be able to combine food materials that do not usually remain mixed together to create food with interesting textures and flavours

Outline information

- Food material – egg yolk
- Working characteristic – egg yolk protein contains an emulsifying agent called **lecithin** which holds oil and water together
- Use in food production – salad dressings, mayonnaise, some reduced fat margarines, baked goods

Technical information

An emulsion is produced when two **immiscible** liquids, such as oil and water, are forced to mix together, when normally they would remain separated. To achieve this two things are needed: vigorous agitation and an emulsifying agent. The emulsifying agent reduces the size of the liquid particles and holds them together in a stable form, where they do not separate when agitated vigorously.

Investigating the working characteristics of egg yolk

Collect:

5 Test tubes and corks
Test tube rack
Cooking oil
Malt vinegar
Salt
Pepper
Egg yolk
Ready-made mustard

1. Label each test tube 1–5
2. Put 15 ml cooking oil and 5 ml Malt vinegar into each one
3. Add different ingredients to each test tube as follows:
   Test tube 1: This is the control sample, add nothing.
   Test tube 2: Add a pinch of salt
   Test tube 3: Add a pinch of salt and a pinch of pepper
   Test tube 4: Add a pinch of salt, a pinch of pepper and 2.5 ml mustard
   Test tube 5: Add a pinch of salt, a pinch of pepper, 2.5 ml mustard and egg yolk
4. Place the corks in each test tube and shake each one vigorously. Place in a test tube rack and note the time
5. Watch carefully and note the time at which each emulsion breaks down into layers

Using your results

- What did you find out about the emulsion?
- What other materials perform a similar function?
- What will be the important features to remember in your designing and making?

Using emulsifiers when designing new products

Look at a range of recipes or food labels which contain emulsifiers. Modify these ideas to design a similar, but new, idea for a summer salad dressing.

Practical investigation 2 – Making mixtures lighter (aeration)

Manufacturers make great use of the ability of eggs, in particular egg white, to hold air, making a mixture lighter in texture and larger in volume.

Outline information

- Food material – egg, particularly egg white
- Working characteristic – whisked egg will become foamy by trapping air
- Use in food production – cold desserts, mousses, meringues, batters and whisked sponge cakes.

Technical information

A foam is produced when a gas is dispersed through a liquid. Egg white (albumin) will produce such a foam when it is whisked. A very fine "honeycomb" structure is created. However the foam is not very stable and it soon returns to a liquid which cannot be re-whisked. Added ingredients will affect the foam, for example, sugar will make it more stable.

Using your results

- What did you find out about the way the egg white performed?
- What will be the important features to remember in your designing and making?

Using foams when designing new foods

Look at a range of recipes or food labels which use the whole egg or egg white to lighten and aerate a product. Modify these ideas to design a similar, but new, idea for a dessert.

Investigating the working characteristics of egg white

Collect:

5 eggs
5 clear measuring jugs
Whisk
Food scales
75 g sugar
Labels 1–5
Digital clock

- Separate each egg, putting equal amounts of egg white in each jug
- Place the yolks in a separate bowl
- Whisk egg white 1 with nothing added until it is firm with pointed peaks. This is the **control**
- Whisk egg white 2 together with 25 g sugar
- Whisk egg white 3 until it is firm and peaks, then whisk in 25 g sugar
- Whisk egg white 4 until it is firm with peaks, whisk in 1 teaspoon sugar from 25 g, fold in the remaining sugar
- Whisk egg white 5 together with half a teaspoon of egg yolk

For each foam record

	Time taken to whisk	Volume of foam after whisking	Volume of foam after 10 minutes	Liquid seepage after 10 minutes
Egg white 1				
Egg white 2				
Egg white 3				
Egg white 4				
Egg white 5				

Functions and characteristics of food materials

Practical investigation 3 – Making mixtures set (coagulation)

Manufacturers often need to make a mixture thicker or hold it in a set shape. They make use of eggs, which harden when heated.

Outline information

- Food material – egg
- Working characteristic – egg protein thickens (**coagulates**) when heated
- Use in food production – savoury flans, quiches, pie fillings, custards, custard tarts and custard pies

Technical information

Egg proteins coagulate when heated, eventually setting to a solid state, as in a boiled egg. When egg is mixed with other liquids such as milk, and then heated the egg can thicken the mixture. When cooled, the mixture will set. Similarly egg can set around solid food such as meat and vegetable mixtures, binding them together and setting around them when heated.

Investigating the working characteristics of eggs

Collect:

4 × 500 ml oven proof bowls
Baking tins
1 litre milk
75 g sugar
6 eggs

1 Set an oven at 160° C or gas mark 4

2 Label each bowl 1–4

3 Prepare each sample by beating together the ingredients as follows:
Sample 1: (Control)
1 egg
250 ml milk
15 g sugar
Sample 2:
2 eggs
250 ml milk
15 g sugar
Sample 3:
1 egg
1 egg yolk
250 ml milk
15 g sugar
Sample 4:
1 egg
250 ml milk
30 g sugar

4 Pour each mixture into its labelled bowl
Place bowl into a baking tin filled with 2 cm water

5 Bake for 40 minutes in an oven set at 160° C or gas mark 4 on the same shelf.

Using your results

- What did you find out about the way the egg set the mixture?
- What other materials perform a similar function?
- What will be the important features to remember in your designing and making?

Using eggs for setting when designing new products

Look at a range of recipes or food packets which contain egg as the setting agent. Modify a vegetarian flan recipe to alter the amount of egg that it contains or to alter the firmness of set required.

Practical investigation 4 – Making mixtures thicker (gelatinisation)

Manufacturers make great use of the ability of starches, in particular flours, to thicken mixtures and help them set.

Outline information

- Food material – various flours
- Working characteristic – many flours will thicken mixtures when heated with a liquid
- Use in food production – sauces, gravies, meat mixtures, fruit fillings, desserts such as custard and blancmange

Technical information

Flours contain a polysaccharide called **starch**. When starch is heated with a liquid, the starch grains soften and swell holding the liquid (gelatinisation). As the mixture cools, the starch causes it to set (gel) to a point when it may be able to hold a definite shape, e.g. animal shaped blancmange from a mould.

Investigating the working characteristics of corn starch

Collect:

Packet of corn starch
5 small saucepans
Thermometer
5 small jelly moulds

1. Prepare 5 identical samples of the following:

   5 g corn starch mixed to a paste with 100 ml cold water (they may be mixed in the saucepans)

   Label the samples 1–5
2. Heat the first sample to 60° C, stirring continuously. Pour into a small jelly mould and leave to cool completely
3. Heat the second sample to 70° C, stirring continuously. Pour into a small jelly mould and leave to cool completely
4. Heat the third sample to 80° C, stirring continuously. Pour into a small jelly mould and leave to cool completely
5. Heat the fourth sample to 90° C, stirring continuously. Pour into a small jelly mould and leave to cool completely
6. Heat the fifth sample to 100° C, stirring continuously. Pour into a small jelly mould and leave to cool completely
7. Compare the results by noticing
   a) colour of the mixture
   b) the thickness of the "set", for example, will the mixture hold its shape if removed from the mould.

Using your results

- What did you find out about the way the starch thickened the mixture?
- What other materials perform a similar function?
- What will be the important features to remember in your designing and making?

Using starch as a thickener when designing new products

- Look at a range of food packets or labels which have starch on the list of ingredients. Find out what starches are used in different products.
- What is meant by modified starch, what products is this used in and what does it do?

Using additives

The food industry has developed a range of food additives to help us manipulate the behaviour of foods. This is important, since consumers demand products that have a certain shelf life. In the UK, unlike in France, we do not buy bread fresh every day, we like to buy bread that will last for at least a few days, so a preservative is added to the bread to stop it drying out and going mouldy too quickly.

Additives are used to:

- Add to product appeal (e.g. glazes, colourings, stabilisers or flavourings can be used to enhance certain aspects of a product's appearance or taste)
- Preserve and keep food safe to eat (e.g. sulphur dioxide can be used to prevent sliced apple from browning)
- Aid the manufacture of foods (e.g. ice-cream can contain alginates E401–405 to help trap air during freezing, in order to make it lighter and softer)
- Enable the addition or removal of a food component (e.g. food gums such as **carageenans** can be used to replace fat in low calorie products).

Above is a list of some additives as a guide. Some can be bought in ordinary shops but you may not be able to use these in school. Knowing that they are available means that you can be more adventurous and realistic in your food design proposals. This should also help you understand the difference between the products you develop in the test kitchen and the ones that are made by food manufacturers in high volume.

Additive	Function
Preservatives	Use to prevent microbial, fungal or mould growth, helps to keep food fresh for longer.
Antioxidants	Inhibits oxidation of fats which cause rancid "off" flavours in fatty foods and oily fish.
Colouring	Either natural or man-made to give colour to food, used a lot in the production of soft drinks.
Flavouring agents	Both natural and synthetic, used to enhance flavours or to replace a food, e.g. strawberry flavour yoghurt may not have any real strawberries in it.
Sweeteners	To make food taste sweet without the calories of sugar, e.g. diet drinks and "lite" foods.
Gelling agents, stabilisers, emulsifiers Modified starches	Used to create or maintain a certain desirable consistency in food, e.g. whipped cream, mousses, desserts. Can add bulk, texture and creaminess to foods which do not naturally have these characteristics. They are more stable at high and low temperatures than corn or wheatflour.

Additions are coded with "E" numbers for easy reference. This means that within the European Economic Community, foods manufactured with "E numbers" can be moved from one country to another. All additives must be cleared for safety and only the permitted amount of each is used in foods. Additives must be listed in the ingredients list on food labels. Their use is controlled by law.

Focused task: Labels

1 Look at food labels from a range of food products similar to the one that you are designing. Select one product with at least three additives in the ingredients list.

2 Take each ingredient, explain why it is there and what its function is.

3 What would happen to the product if any of the ingredients were left out? Why do you think this particular ingredient was chosen? How do you think the product was processed?

Practical investigation

If you do this practical as a group, you can choose different items from the list below. Make a basic salad dressing and divide into 2 samples. Keep one sample as the control. To the second sample, add one of the ingredients below to simulate additive use. Compare the 2 samples.

- Lemon juice – for its ascorbic acid content (an antioxidant), or half a vitamin C tablet
- Gelatin, pectin or carageenan – to thicken and act as an emulsifier
- Food colouring – to enhance colour
- Herbs – to develop a distinctive flavour
- Vinegar (acetic acid) – an acidic preservative to keep the product longer
- Egg – contains emulsifiers which will help mix oil and vinegar together.

Basic recipe

- 3 parts salad oil (e.g. 30 ml)
- 1 part vinegar (e.g. 10 ml)
- One chosen "additive":
  - Powdered or sheet gelatine dissolved in warm water according to the instructions on the package **or** carageenan or pectin powder blended with a small amount of salt or sugar and then mixed with some warm water using a whisk
  - 15 ml lemon juice or a vitamin C tablet dissolved in a tablespoon of water
  - 1–5 ml food colouring mixed gradually, using a pipette or teaspoon
  - 15 g fresh herbs or 5 g dried herbs
  - 1 part extra vinegar
  - Whole powdered (pasteurised) egg instead of fresh. Follow the instructions on the packet, mixing a small amount of powder with water using a whisk. Add to your oil and vinegar very gradually while mixing.

Method

1. Weigh out or measure the basic ingredients.
2. Mix all your ingredients vigorously together using a whisk, blender or food mixer.
3. Pour half the mixture into a clean jar or bottle and label it "control sample".
4. Now take the remaining sample and mix in your prepared additive.
5. Store at room temperature for at least a week.
6. Organise a taste panel to try your product on a basic lettuce salad and record your results.

Nutrition and product development

Sometimes, when we are involved in the excitement of product development, it is easy to forget why we eat food! Food is necessary to keep us alive and healthy. It provides us with the nutrients and energy we need for basic bodily functions such as breathing, circulation, digestion, growth, cell repair and protection against infection, as well as what is needed for movement and activity.

Food manufacturers may consider the following during new product development:

- Food products provide people with nutrients which are vital to health and well-being. The nutritional value of food is, therefore, one of the criteria in defining the quality of any food product and the nutrient profile may be included in the product specification.
- Nutritional information displayed on food packaging and information about food product contents has to be very accurate.
- Nutrients in foods are affected by the way food is processed during manufacture.
- Some products are designed to meet particular dietary needs and so nutrition will be a significant part of the product concept.

Food technologists liaise with nutritionists when they are designing products. The nutritionist advises on: nutritional content, product development, how products may be modified, nutritional labelling and cooking and storage instructions. You too will need to develop and apply your understanding of nutrition when you are designing and making food products.

The main food groups

Food contains nutrients which are chemical components needed by humans to maintain life and health. The main nutrients are: carbohydrate, fat, protein, vitamins and minerals. There are two other non-nutrients which are essential to life – water and fibre (or non starch polysaccharide). Water is necessary because all our body processes depend on water. Fibre (NSP) is not digested, but it aids digestion by adding bulk to the diet and assisting the removal of waste products in the faeces.

Nutrition and product development

Healthy eating

Healthy, or balanced, eating is about making sure that you eat the right combinations of a variety of foods which provide the nutrients necessary for well being.

The Health of the Nation (1992) document sets out the Department of Health's plans to achieve improved health for the people of this country. The nutrition targets by the year 2005 are:

- to reduce the average percentage of food energy from total fat from about 40% to no more than about 35%
- to reduce the average percentage of food energy from saturated fatty acids from about 17% to no more than 11%
- to reduce the proportion of men aged 16–64 who are obese by at least 25% and the number of women by at least 33%.

In 1992, the Nutrition Task Force was set up to prepare a plan to achieve the targets above. It is working with the food industry to explore the setting of targets for product development and marketing food products. This might mean, for example, that the industry agrees to work towards a reduction of fat and saturated fatty acid content of existing and new products.

Food groups and choices

Five food groups	Bread, other cereals and potatoes	Fruit and vegetables	Milk and dairy foods	Meat, fish and alternatives	Fatty and sugary foods
Types of foods	All types of bread rolls, chapati, crumpets, crackers, rice cakes, naan. All types of grain e.g. oats, barley, rye. 'Other cereals' means things like breakfast cereals, pasta, rice, noodles. (Beans and lentils can be eaten as part of this group.)	Fresh, frozen and canned fruit and vegetables and dried fruit, fruit juice. (Beans and lentils can be eaten as part of this group.)	Milk, cheese, yoghurt and fromage frais. (This group does not contain butter, eggs and cream.)	Meat, poultry, fish, eggs, nuts, seeds, beans and lentils. Meat includes bacon and salami, meat products, beefburgers. All the different varieties of canned beans are in this group. Fish includes frozen and canned fish, fish fingers and fish cakes.	Margarine, low-fat spread, butter, ghee, cooking oils, oily salad dressing, cream, chocolate, crisps, biscuits, rich sauces, sweets and sugar, fizzy soft drinks, puddings.
Main nutrients	Carbohydrate (starch), fibre, some calcium and iron, B-group vitamins.	Vitamin C, carotenes, iron, calcium, folate, fibre and some carbohydrate.	Calcium, protein, B-group vitamins especially B12, vitamins A and D.	Iron, protein, B-group vitamins, especially B12, zinc and magnesium.	Some vitamins and essential fatty acids but also a lot of fat, sugar and salt.
How much to choose	Eat lots.	Eat lots, try to have five servings every day.	Eat moderate amounts and choose lower-fat versions whenever you can.	Eat moderate amounts and choose lower-fat versions whenever you can.	Eat fatty and sugary foods sparingly – that is infrequently or in small amounts.
What types to choose	Try to eat wholemeal, wholegrain, brown or high-fibre versions where possible. Try to avoid having them fried too often (e.g. chips), adding too much fat (e.g. thickly spread butter), adding rich sauces and dressings such as mayonnaise.	Eat a wide variety of fruit and vegetables. Try to avoid adding fat and rich sauces to vegetables, adding sugar and syrupy dressings to fruit (e.g. adding chocolate sauce to banana).	Lower-fat versions include semi-skimmed or skimmed milk, low-fat yoghurts or fromage frais and lower-fat cheeses. Check the fat content by looking at the labels – compare and choose the lowest.	Lower-fat versions include meat with the fat cut off, poultry without the skin and fish without batter. Cook these foods without added fat. Beans and lentils are good alternatives to meat as they are very low in fat and high in fibre.	Some foods from this group will probably be eaten every day, but should be kept to small amounts, such as margarine, low-fat spreads. Other foods in this group may be eaten occasionally, but should not replace foods from the four main groups.

Source: 'The Balance of Good Health', Health Education Authority

The Ministry of Agriculture, Fisheries and Food (MAFF) has produced eight guidelines:

- enjoy your food
- eat a variety of different foods
- eat the right amount to be a healthy weight for your height
- eat plenty of foods rich in starch and fibre
- don't eat too much fat
- don't eat sugary foods too often
- store and prepare foods carefully so that their vitamins and minerals are not lost
- if you drink alcohol, keep within sensible limits.

"The Balance of Good Health" (1994) uses a diagram of a dinner plate to show the proportions of the different basic food groups which people are advised to eat. The key message is that balanced eating can be achieved over time, if you use the plate as a guide to choosing foods. It is what you eat over a period of time rather than on any one particular day, that will affect future health.

Using nutritional guidelines

Dietary guidelines are standards, advice and information about nutritional needs. Food manufacturers will refer to these to plan products or meals so that they contain the recommended nutritional requirements.

Dietary Reference Values (DRVs) give an indication of the nutritional requirements of different people who are in good health. They give several figures to cover the needs of most healthy people in the population, and recognise that even within one group of people, some will have higher or lower requirements than others. Two DRVs which are commonly used are RNI and EARs. DRV tables are produced by the Department for Health ("COMA Report 41").

- **Reference Nutrient Intake** (RNI) is the amount of nutrient that is thought to cover the needs of almost everyone in a particular group. Used for proteins, vitamins and minerals.
- **Estimated Average Requirements** (EARs) is the DRV which is used for energy.
- **Lower Reference Nutrient Intake** (LRNI) is the amount of a nutrient which is enough for a very small proportion of the population who have particularly low needs.
- **Safe Intake** is the term used to indicate an amount of a nutrient that is enough for almost everyone, but not so large as to cause undesired effects.

Different nutritional needs

People's nutritional needs change throughout their lives. Childhood, for example, is a period of rapid growth and development when nutritional needs are high. Men and women tend to have different nutritional and energy needs because of physical differences between them. People who are physically very active in their work or social lives, will have higher energy needs than people who are less active. Nutritional requirements will reflect these general differences.

There are people who have special dietary needs, such as vegetarians or people with allergies or food intolerances (lactose or gluten intolerance).

Focused task: Dietary analysis

1. Keep a record of a friend, neighbour or relative's diet over a week. Carry out an analysis of the main nutrients which their diet contains. Evaluate their diet against the recommended DRVs for their age, sex and occupational group. Take into account any special dietary needs they may have. Provide them with some feedback and suggestions about how they might improve their diet.
2. Find out about one special dietary need and design a new product for that need.

Focused task: Dietary needs

Choose a food product, e.g. a ready meal. Use the nutritional information provided on the label to calculate the contribution it makes to the daily diet of someone your age.

Understanding nutrition through IT

Computer software programmes can be used to calculate the nutritional content (profile) of specific foods, recipes, dishes or products. You will need to enter data such as amounts, weights or portion sizes and the foods you want to analyse. The computer will then provide data in the form of a nutritional breakdown and it can be produced as a chart or graph. You can also manipulate and alter ratios and proportions of a recipe or formulation.

Focused task: Product analysis

Take two products, e.g. a regular cauliflower cheese and "lite" or low fat cauliflower cheese, or a regular tinned soup and a reduced calorie version of the same soup.

1. Use the nutritional labels to analyse and compare your two products. Use the product label to work out how the product has been modified.
2. Use a nutritional software programme to try some modelling. Alter or substitute ingredients in a recipe to see how they affect the nutritional profile of a product.

Nutritional claims

Manufacturers often make claims about the nutritional content of their products. This is part of their marketing strategy for the products. Many people, for example, are attracted by claims that a product has a reduced fat content. Food legislation sets some standards and rules for the claims which can be made legitimately, to prevent people giving false information. By law, the manufacturers have to back up their claims by providing nutritional information on the product label. Information may be given per 100 ml or 100 g and may also be given per portion.

Case study – Lower fat products

McVitie's *Go Ahead!* is a range of biscuits, cakes and savoury snacks which contain lower levels of fat. The packet contains an information panel helping you to count the amount of fat which the *Go Ahead!* products contain.

Since the "Sticky Syrup" and "Fruit Bars" claim to be 97% fat free the manufacturer has to include nutritional information on the pack. It gives average values per 100 g of the product and per cake.

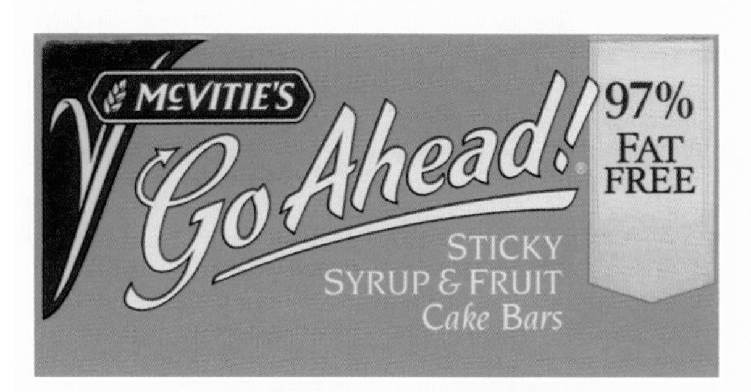

INGREDIENTS: Wheat Flour, Sultanas (14%), Partially Inverted Sugar Syrup, Grated Carrot, Raisins (8%), Invert Sugar Syrup, Egg Whites, Glycerine, Whole Egg, Water, Sugar, Stabilizer (Sorbitol), Vegetable Oil and Hydrogenated Vegetable Oil, Raising Agents (Acid Sodium Pyrophosphate, Sodium Bicarbonate), Emulsifiers (E471, E435, E475), Defatted Soya Flour, Dextrose Monohydrate, Salt, Modified Starch, Ground Nutmeg, Ground Cinnamon, Preservative (Potassium Sorbate).

Store in a cool, dry place.

NUTRITION INFORMATION	AVERAGE VALUES	
	Per 100g	Per Cake
ENERGY	1199 kJ 283 kcal	441 kJ 104 kcal
PROTEIN	5.0 g	1.8 g
CARBOHYDRATE	62.5 g	23.0 g
of which Sugars	40.3 g	14.8 g
FAT	2.7 g	1.0 g
of which Saturates	1.0 g	0.4 g
FIBRE	2.0 g	0.7 g
SODIUM	0.4 g	0.1 g

McVitie's Quality:
We take every care to ensure that McVitie's Go Ahead products reach you in perfect condition. If they fail to satisfy, please return the complete package to our Quality Assurance Department at the address below, saying when and where purchased.

MADE IN UK BY McVITIE'S, PO BOX 117, STAINES, MIDDLESEX, TW18 3PH

5 000168 020334 >

Focused task

Note the calorific value of a number of similar biscuits which claim to be low fat, low sugar or low calorie. Make a note of their fat and sugar contents and their overall calorific value per 100 g and/or per biscuit. Record the information in a table or spreadsheet, so that you can make comparisons.

Is a low fat or low sugar product always low in calories? Explain your findings.

Food processing

On a production line, food materials pass through a number of processes in sequence. Ingredients are introduced into the line at appropriate points and processed by machines in a variety of ways, e.g. cooking, shaping, drying, chilling. The product is then finished, assembled and packaged.

During processing, food is treated in such a way that its nature and properties are changed:

- to improve its eating quality
- to create a useful ingredient
- to preserve it.

Shredding

Mixing

Adding mayonnaise

Packaging

Focused task: ***Reasons for processing***

Copy the table below and give examples in the appropriate columns

Improved eating quality	Create an ingredient	To preserve it
meat is cooked	extract juice from fruit	frozen peas

Unit operations

All food processing requires a combination of procedures to change the raw materials into the final product. These are known as **unit operations**. A number of unit operations are grouped together to form a process. The combination and sequence of unit operations determines the final product.

Method of processing	Unit operations	Examples
Ambient Temperature Processing	Handling raw materials	Preparation of raw materials – cleaning, peeling
	Size reduction	Slicing, dicing, pulping, grinding
	Mixing and forming	Mixing different foods together – dough, diced vegetables Forming (shaping) – bread, biscuits, pasta, chocolate, sweets
	Separating	Separating foods – squeezing juice, filtering, pressing
	Fermenting	Lactic acid fermentation – yogurt production, pickles, cottage cheese Alcohol fermentation – dough, drinks
	Enzyme technology	Pectic enzyme for juice clarification Protease – meat tenderising
	Irradiation	For food preservation
Processing by the Application of Heat	Heat processing using steam or water	Blanching – frozen vegetable production Concentrating – tomato puree, jamming, sauces, syrups Pasteurising – milk, juices, syrups, bottling Sterilising – canned foods, UHT cartons Extrusion – snack foods, breakfast cereals, T.V.P.
	Heat processing using hot air	Sun drying – tomatoes, apricots Artificial drying – onion rings, pears, herbs Baking – biscuits, cakes, bread Roasting – nuts
	Heating by irradiated energy	Thawing out, defrosting fish, meat, butter and other fats Drying – crispbreads
	Heat processing using oil	Shallow frying – burgers Deep frying – snack foods, chips, samosas, doughnuts
Processing by the Removal of Heat	Chilling	Used for fresh foods – meat, fish, dairy products Cook–chill dishes or meals
	Controlled Atmosphere Storage Modified Atmosphere Packaging	Fruit and vegetables Salads, pasta, meat
	Freezing	Fresh produce – meat, fish, fruit and vegetables, ice cream Ready prepared produce – pastry, sausages, breaded fish, rolls Cooked produce – pies, pastries
	Freeze drying and freeze concentration	Coffee and fruit juices
Post-processing Operations	Food finishing	Coating in cereal crumbs – Scotch eggs Enrobing in batters – fish, mushrooms, vegetables
	Packaging food	Protecting food Promoting food
	Material handling and process control	Ordering, moving and storing Quality assurance from raw materials to end product

Product life and maintenance

When designing a new food product, a manufacturer has to consider the product's life:

- How long will consumers expect this food product to last before eating it?
- How are they going to carry it home?
- How are they going to store it?

It is the manufacturer's job to ensure that the quality of the product is good after it has been stored and then reheated by the consumer. They have to think about:

- the kind of processing that will give the shelf life expected by the consumer
- how to package the product so that it is not damaged when it is transported or stored
- how additional techniques or ingredients can be used to improve shelf life or quality (e.g. modified air packaging or additives).

A food manufacturer will have to provide the consumer with clear instructions on storage and cooking or reheating. They will test the product in a number of ways to get this information.

Bacteriological testing

Food spoilage and preservation

All food in its natural form, begins the process of decay once it has been slaughtered or harvested. Cell walls begin to break down, allowing the loss of nutrients. Very soon there are visible signs of deterioration, where micro-organisms have attacked the food.

Preservation is a treatment given to food, that prolongs the period for which it remains edible. Preservation alters conditions so that microbial life is more difficult. Optimum conditions for microbial life include the following:

Heat – average optimum for most microbes is 37° C
Type of food – high protein foods
Oxygen – aerobic, anaerobic, facultatively anaerobic
pH – average optimum pH 7
Time – binary fission every twenty minutes
Moisture – damp conditions

Thermal processes make foods safer and preserve them by reducing the action of enzymes, micro-organisms and chemical reactions which cause undesirable spoilage. Thermal processes enable us to have convenience foods and make it easier to transport products. You may have heard of some of these: spray drying (e.g. instant packet soups), freeze drying (e.g. freeze dried coffee) and concentration (e.g. evaporated milk).

Thermal processing

Conveyor oven

Thermally processing meat

Freezing

Cherry cooling

Yoghurt manufacture

Sausage rolls

The heating and cooling of foods is used to preserve and extend shelf life of food products and to improve palatability (e.g. freezing, chilling, cooking, pasteurizing).

Soup manufacture

Product life and maintenance

Process	Main purpose	Example of product	Temperature/ time	Example of equipment used
Blanching	To destroy enzymes	Peas for freezing	100 °C/2 minutes	Steam blanchers
Pasteurization	To destroy disease-forming micro-organisms, enzymes inactive	Milk Orange juice	71.5 °C/15 seconds 88 °C/15 seconds	Plate heat exchanger Tubular heat exchanger
Sterilisation	To destroy all micro-organisms	Baby food (in jars) Long-life fruit juice (in cartons)	135 °C/28 minutes 150 °C/1 second	Rotary retort Steam injection
Chilling	To reduce multiplication rate of micro-organisms	Yoghurts	3 °C	Refrigerator or blast chiller
Freezing	To halt microbial development	Frozen vegetables Frozen meat	−18 °C −30 °C	Domestic freezer Commercial blast freezer

To demonstrate how thermal processing fits into a production line and why it is used, we will look at the processing of canned peas as an example. Ringed processes in the diagram are thermal.

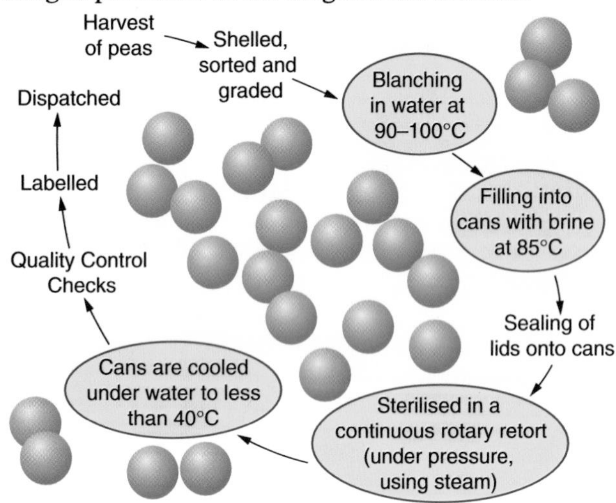

Thermal processing of milk

Pasteurization – the process of heating milk to a high enough temperature, for the right amount of time, to kill harmful organisms such as Salmonella, Campylobacter. The modern method for pasteurization is the high temperature, short time (HTST) one, which is 71.7 °C for 15 seconds.

Sterilization – the temperature of sterilization for milk is 120 °C for 15 minutes. The traditional method is by "in-bottle" sterilization, in which milk is poured into the bottle and sealed.

Ultra heat treatment (UHT) – "long-life" milk is heated to 132 °C for 1 second, cooled and poured into pre-sterilized bottles or cartons.

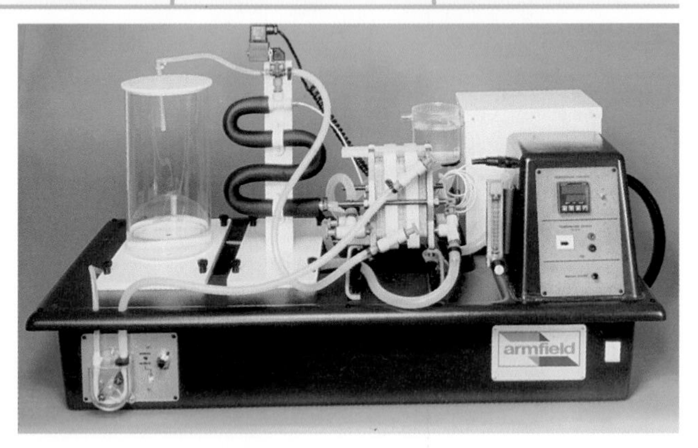

Small-scale pasteurizer

Refrigeration and freezing

As the temperature decreases, the growth of most micro-organisms slows down. However, Listeria and Yersinia are examples of organisms which are able to survive at temperatures below 10 °C and they can still multiply and cause illness. Most foods benefit from quick freezing or "blast freezing", because it causes less damage to the cells but still prevents spoilage.

Accuracy of thermal processing

Over-processing can damage a product's flavour, texture and nutrient content, as well as wasting energy and time. Under-processing may leave food unsafe to eat and with a shortened shelf life. For example, freshly squeezed orange juice has a stronger, fresher taste, brighter colour and sometimes more vitamin C than long-life orange juice, which has been sterilized at a high temperature. This is because the heat destroys delicate aromatic flavours, caramelizes sugars in the fruit juice, giving a slight brown colour, and destroys vitamin C.

For efficient heating or cooling, it is necessary to optimise heat transfer by conduction, convection and radiation, appropriate to different foods.

Stop and think

- How could you cool down hot soup quickly and safely?
- Why do you stir liquids as they are heated up?
- What happens to the surface of a food when you grill it?

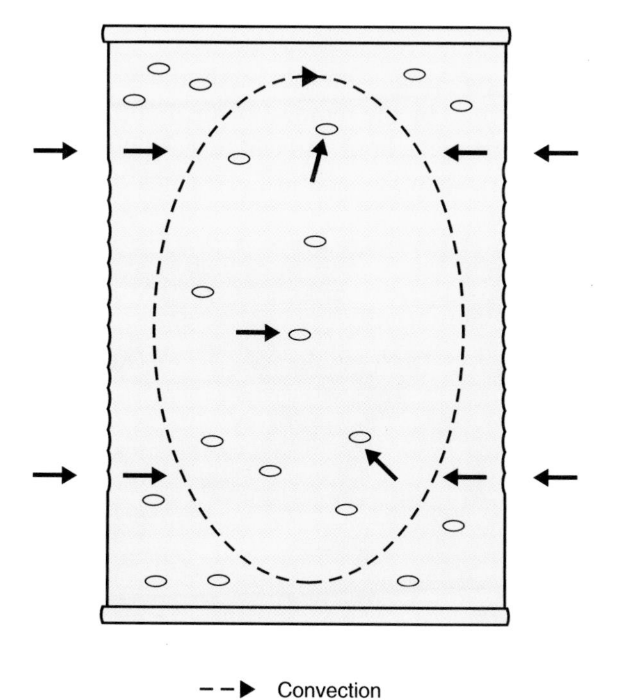

Remember when you are thermally processing foods:

- Foods heat up and cool down at different rates, e.g. milk heats up more quickly than a thicker (more **viscous**) custard which will therefore require agitation and a longer time to heat through.
- Some foods provide better growing conditions for harmful micro-organisms than others, and require more severe heat treatment, e.g. corned beef can contain Clostridium botulinum spores, which cause botulism, and must be treated at 121.1 °C for at least 40 minutes to be sterilized. On the other hand, tomato soup does not provide good growing conditions for many micro-organisms, so 100 °C for 20 minutes is sufficient.

Many different types of equipment are used to thermally process foods industrially.

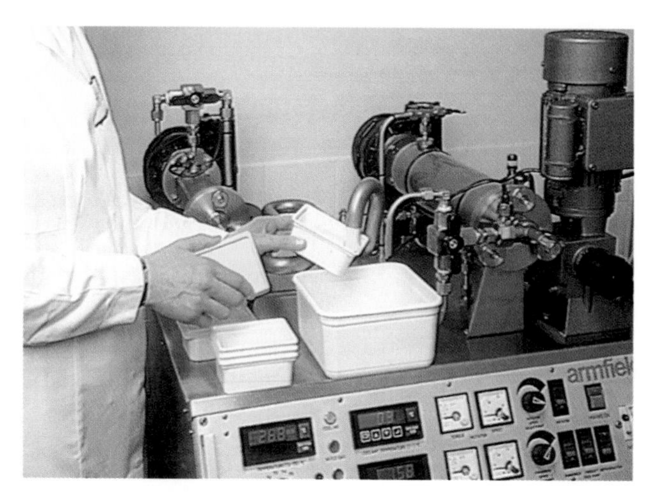

Margarine crystallizer

Spray drier

Product life and maintenance

Removal of water

Most micro-organisms need water to grow so if the water is removed from foods they cannot. Foods can also be preserved (for example by **dehydration**) if the water is made unavailable for growth. The amount of available water in a food is described in terms of the **water activity** (Aw). Moisture levels are compared to pure water, having an Aw of 1.0. Chemically-bound water has an Aw of 0.0.

Approximate pH value and water activity (Aw) of some common foods

Food	pH range	Aw
Poultry	6.2–6.4	0.985
Fish	6.6–6.8	0.985
Milk	6.3–6.8	0.98–0.99
Mayonnaise	3.0–3.8	0.92–0.93
Beef (Ground)	5.1–6.2	0.98
Ham	5.9–6.1	0.85–0.95
Cheese	4.9–5.9	0.85–0.92
Cooked chill meal*	4.0–6.5	0.95–0.98

* Particularly variable depending on the type and composition of the sauce and the amount of particulate matter (i.e. solid : liquid ratio).

There are several methods that are used for the drying of foodstuffs. These are listed below:

- spray drying
- kiln drying
- sun drying
- fluidised bed drying
- freeze drying
- drum or roller drying
- tunnel drying
- warm air drying.

Focused task

Choose one of the drying methods listed above and find out what equipment is used, what foods it is used for, how it works, and the advantages and disadvantages of this method.

Acids/pH

Most bacteria grow best under conditions of pH neutrality (about 7). pH is a scale used to measure acidity and alkalinity. Acids have a pH of 1–7 and alkalines 7–14. Pickles and salad creams are "self stable" because they contain acetic acid (vinegar) and have a low pH level. Fruit drinks are relatively free from spoilage because they contain citric acid, and carbonated drinks because they contain carbonic acid.

How is the pH level measured in the food industry?

Removal of air/oxygen

Canned goods are heat-treated to ensure the contents are free from pathogenic bacteria. The environment in a can is anaerobic. What does this term mean? Clostridium botulinum is an **anaerobic** organism, and if present in the can, could multiply given the correct conditions. Therefore, in the food industry, canned goods are placed in a **retort**, and every particle of food is heated to 121° C for at least three minutes. This is known as the **"botulinum cook"**. With large cans of stodgy contents, the time factor may be increased to achieve this temperature. What effect does this have on the contents of the can?

Vacuum packing is another method which preserves food by the removal of air. Food packages have the air sucked out and can be gas flushed to extend their shelf life. Name a gas which is used in this process.

Focused task: Thermally processing soup

You are a manufacturer producing a soup to sell to a Supermarket chain.

- What appropriate thermal processing options are there?
- How can you thermally process it?
- What are the advantages and disadvantages of each option?

Here is an example from a student who was working on sauces. Use the example to help you do the task.

Pasta sauce

	Cook–chill	Sterilised	Dried
Process	The sauce will be cooked to temp of approx 70–85 °C for a few minutes then packaged and immediately cooled to less than 5 °C	UHT and aseptically packaged (tetrapak) or canned. Heated to 95–121 °C for 15–30 mins	Freeze dried (at 240 °C under vacuum) or spray dried (at 170–200 °C)
Advantages	Fresh "home cooked" flavour and colour. Consumer associates with high quality.	Long shelf life of over one year. Convenient, no need to refrigerate.	Long shelf life of over one year. Low transport costs, light weight, convenient.
Disadvantages	Short shelf life, expensive packaging. Often more wastage. Only seasonal ingredients can be used.	Loss of colour, texture flavour and some vitamins.	Need rehydrating.Small loss of colour, flavour and nutrients. Expensive.

Focused task: Investigating shelf life

Here is a test that you can carry out on your product:

1. Make a food product from your own recipe.
2. Divide it into 4 equal portions and wrap them in appropriate packaging material.
3. Label each sample and store as follows:

Portion 1 is the **control** and used for comparison with the other samples.
Portion 2 is to be stored at ambient (room) temperature.
Portion 3 is to be **chilled** at 5 °C temperature.
Portion 4 is to be **frozen** (– 18 °C).

DO NOT EAT FOOD after storage without first consulting your teacher.

4. Compare each sample with the control for any changes in:
   - appearance
   - colour (surface and internal)
   - texture and consistency
   - smell
   - evidence of yeasts, moulds or bacteria.

Sample 2 and 3 (ambient and chilled storage):
Inspect the state of the food at 2 days, 4 days and 6 days

Sample 4 (frozen storage):
Inspect at 1 week, 2 weeks and 3 weeks

Consider the changes that have taken place. You may need to modify the product so that the shelf life could be extended.

The effects of processing on nutritional content

The ways in which foods are prepared, cooked and stored will affect the nutritional content of the end product. Think about this when deciding on preparation and processing methods during product development.

The nutritional value of proteins, fats and carbohydrates is little affected by preparation and cooking. However some vitamins are less stable as the chart below shows. There is some vitamin loss in most methods of processing foods, especially with the water soluble vitamins B and C.

Process	Vitamin/Characteristics
Storage (time)	Some vitamins are lost by enzyme activity and oxidation during storage, especially at room temperature, particularly Vitamin C.
Cooking	Vitamins A, D, E and K which are soluble in fat will be lost in grilling, but frying will increase these vitamins. Vitamin B group is water soluble. There will be some loss in cooking water and by oxidation when food is cut and shredded. There is greatest loss in large volumes of cooking water. Very sensitive to the effect of heat and destroyed at higher temperatures. Vitamin B1 is destroyed in alkaline solution. Vitamin C (water soluble) Some loss in cooking water and by oxidation when food is cut or shredded. The greatest loss in large volumes of water. Very sensitive to the effects of heat and destroyed at higher/low temperatures. Speed of destruction is increased in alkaline solution.
Drying	Vitamin B1 and C are lost in drying.
Canning/vacuuming	Vitamin C is lost, although chemicals my be added to preserve the vitamin content.
Freezing	Vitamin loss in frozen foods is often low because of the efficiency and speed of the transportation from the processing plant to freezing and packing. Some vitamin C is lost in the blanching process and if frozen foods are kept for over a year.

Focused task: Nutrient loss

1 Select a vegetable soup recipe and use the chart showing the effects of food processing on nutrient to work out the best methods for preparing, processing and cooking the ingredients so that as many of the nutrients as possible are retained. Produce your ideas as a chart with the following headings: ingredient, method of preparation or cooking, reason for choice.

2 Some processing methods involve adding nutrients, e.g. fortification of breakfast cereals. Find out about one of these products.

3 Collect together samples of a food that have been processed in different ways. Complete the chart below to analyse their shelf life, additives used, storage, preparation, convenience and cost.

Food	1	2	3	4
Shelf life				
Additives used				
Storage				
Preparation				
Convenience				
Cost				

MANUFACTURING

This section will help you to consider questions to do with manufacturing in volume. Products that you manufacture in school may be one-offs, or prototypes for a small batch or higher volume production. Understanding how the manufacturing industry produces large numbers of products will help you to make appropriate decisions.

You will need to consider how you can manufacture your product(s) to the quality that is needed and, if you are planning volume production, how your methods will differ from one-off production.

Whatever your scale of production you can improve your work by using a systematic approach.

Manufacturing as a system
Routes Core Book page 118

Keeping a **systems overview** of your product can help you to:

- better organise and carry out your manufacturing
- maintain and improve the quality of your product as it develops
- understand industrial manufacturing practices.

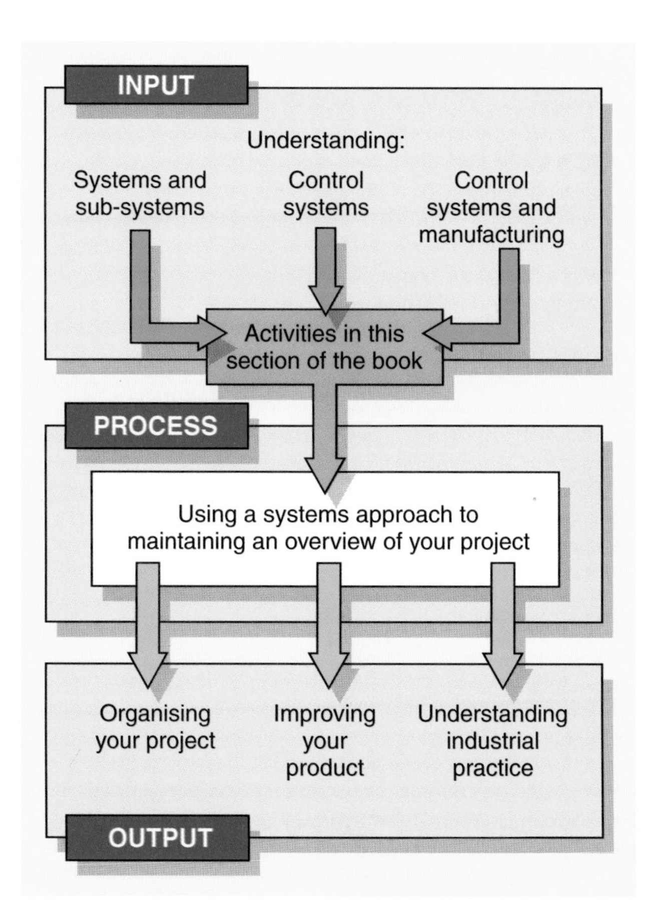

The difference between one-off and high volume production

The aim of food manufacturing is to produce edible products which are fit for human consumption and meet a number of our needs. There are different scales of production, which require different machines, tools and equipment:

- individual one-off crafted products
- batch production, where more than one of the same product is produced at the same time
- mass, continuous or volume production on a much larger scale.

Some large-scale manufacturing processes are carried out in a similar way to food production at school or home, while others require more specialised industrial equipment.

The difference between one-off and high volume production

Developing prototypes and scaling up

Food manufacturers have to be able to create a product that gets consistently good results every time without fail.

To do this they have to know:

- exactly what, and how much, goes into it
- at what point each ingredient is added
- how long it is cooked for
- what temperature it is cooked at
- the exact variety of each ingredient and its country of origin.

Samples prepared in the test kitchen, which have been approved, now become the **reference sample** or **benchmark** for all future development. This means that reproducing them perfectly, whenever required, must be possible throughout the year in a factory situation. This is when it may be decided whether the proposed product has commercial potential.

There are two aspects to accuracy:

1 Accurately recording small-scale benchwork when you are developing the recipe.
2 Making a checklist showing selection, functionality and legislation of all ingredients. These are known as the product parameters and form the official product specification that will be written.

Focused task: Recording small-scale bench work accurately

Equipment needed

scientific digital scales to record to 1 decimal point
stopwatch to record all cooking times
ruler to measure the size composite ingredients are cut to, e.g. diced carrots
paper and pencil

Method

1 All ingredients: raw materials must be weighed as their prepared weight, e.g. onions after you peel them.
2 Record and measure the sizes that all composite ingredients should be prepared to, e.g. cut onion to 5 mm dice.
3 Time all cooking and mixing episodes in the recipe, e.g. frying onions.
4 Record the desired effect from each cooking episode, e.g. fry onions until soft and translucent but not brown.
5 Any alterations to the original formulation must be recorded, e.g. if you added more of any ingredient such as salt.
6 Record the type of equipment used, e.g. manufacturer, model number of a food processor and attachment used. The same applies to cooker make and fuel type.
7 It is important that seasoning is recorded accurately as this may be disastrous at scale-up time.

Case study: One chilli or 1%?

The chef in the test kitchen made a product using fresh chillies, but instead of weighing the chilli, he simply specified one chilli. When the first factory trial was carried out, the factory manager was very angry. The chillies were all different sizes and the hotness of the product could not be controlled because the chef had not specified country of origin or variety.

Maryland cookies

Ingredients	%	Quantity (g)
Biscuit flour	100	6000
Icing sugar	30	1800
Granulated sugar	20	1200
Golden syrup	3.5	210
White vegetable fat	42	2520
Butter	7.5	450
Milk powder	6.5	390
Salt	1	60
Sodium bicarbonate	0.8	48
Cream powder	1.1	66
Vanilla	0.2	12cc
Chocolate chips	30	1800
Roasted hazelnuts	13.5	810
Water	17	1020

In this table ingredients are expressed as percentages of the main ingredient (biscuit flour) as well as by weight so that each ingredient is proportionately accurate when scaled-up to make a large amount.

Focused task: Using a checklist of ingredients and raw materials

Selection

- Are the ingredients suitable for your product?
- Do they match the preferences of your user group?
- Will they be readily available commercially? (in large quantities of consistent quality throughout the year)
- Do they satisfy legal requirements of labelling and claims, e.g. low fat?

Functionality

- Are they technically right for the proposed product?
- Will they be the most profitable?

Legal issues

- Are the ingredients permitted for use in food?
- Are they permitted for use in your proposed product, e.g. a product which is low in cholesterol?

Once you have sourced all your raw ingredients and accurately recorded your recipe, which is now becoming a product formulation, you can take the product into the factory for a trial.

Planning large-scale manufacturing

Production involves the careful management of resources, equipment and time.

Raw materials and supplies

Large-scale manufacture begins with the delivery of raw materials from approved sources or suppliers. The delivery of materials to the factory is co-ordinated so that supplies arrive just before they are needed. Laboratory and other quality checks are carried out against the specification to approve or reject the order, e.g. the specification may include the percentage moisture, protein, fat or salt, and the colour, texture and flavour levels for the materials.

All batches of raw material are coded and a stock control system is used to make sure that materials are used in rotation, with the oldest being used up first. They will be stored under controlled conditions appropriate to the ingredients, e.g. ambient temperature, freezer or cold store.

Case study: Raw material specification

Scotia Haven Foods use raw material purchasing specifications for all the dried fruit, nuts, cereals and pulses they buy. After processing and packing, these are sold to retailers or to food manufacturers such as bakeries or breakfast cereal producers. Each manufacturer has its own specification for each ingredient. The quality assurance controller prepares criteria for each ingredient. Here is the example for California raisins.

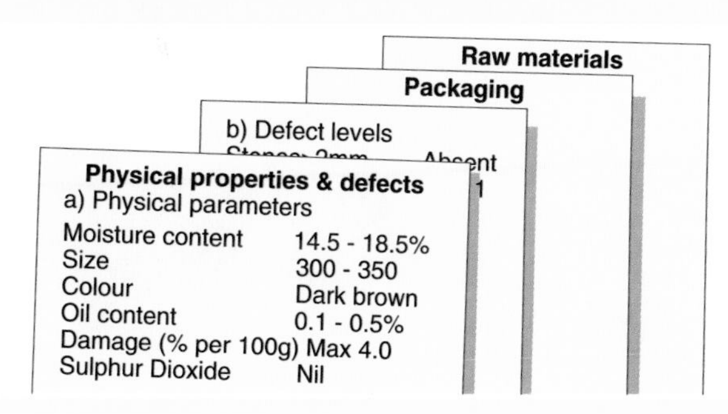

MANUFACTURING

Planning equipment and tools

When manufacturers consider ideas for a new product they have to think about the following:

- What equipment do I currently have?
- What can the current equipment make?
- Can attachments be purchased to make the machine do more functions?
- Does the factory have the capacity to make a new product?
- Do processes need to be altered to make this new recipe work?
- Do any of the ingredients or the final product need special storage or handling?
- What type of packaging is being used? Will this require any special treatment, i.e. grilling products in plastic trays?

Focused task: Stock control system

Set up a system for managing and controlling the stock which is used for practical food technology lessons. Your stock-control system would need to be maintained over a period of time, say, one term. This could be for your class or for all classes which use the food technology room. Allocate roles or take it in turns to monitor and manage the system. Try to incorporate the appropriate use of a computer in your stock-control system. Decide on the evaluation criteria and evaluate the strengths and weaknesses for the system you used.

Choosing the right equipment

1 Every time you start a project, think carefully about which equipment you will use. Set up a test to try out several different pieces of equipment which do the same job. Choose the one which gives you the best results, using the amount of materials. Sometimes a compromise has to be made between quality and quantity.

2 List all the mixers in the food technology room, this should include hand blenders, food processors and large food mixers. Once this list is completed, find out what attachments are available. Your research could include looking at specialist magazines to find out about ribbon mixers, high speed and sheer mixers.

Case study: Rodway Repast

Rodway Repast started manufacturing over 7 years ago, when the managing director, Imogen Applegate, found that there was a gap in the market place for pre-prepared meals. Starting from her own kitchen, she developed a range of dishes, including lasagne and pasta dishes.

When Imogen Applegate was assessing the factory for future use, she decided to make an **inventory** (list) of all the current equipment that the company owned both in current production and storage. She then recorded the equipment's age and uses and found out what upgrades and attachments were available. She found that the factory had a lot of general mixers but only a few specialist mixers and extruders. However, two general mixers were suitable to be upgraded.

The small cost of the new upgraded equipment was quickly recouped, as the factory could make meatballs and savoury samosas with this new equipment.

Time planning

Manufacturing a fast-moving product

Time is an important consideration to food manufacturers. Often the raw ingredients arrive at the factory and are processed into the finished product within 24 hours! This is because fresh-food ingredients have to be used quickly or they deteriorate and once the product is finished, it has to be delivered to the consumer quickly to be eaten at its best. Sometimes manufacturers choose particular ingredients, processes and equipment to give them more time. These are thought about carefully when designing.

This manufacturer uses dried mushrooms in the product because they can be bought in bulk, are always available and keep longer. This saves money and time as they need less preparation. She compared the product with one made with fresh mushrooms, but felt that the gain in taste was not enough to justify the extra expense.

Sequencing tasks

The food industry use Gantt charts to sequence all their tasks.

Activities	WEEK 1	WEEK 2	WEEK 3	WEEK 4
Market Research				
Evaluating				
Generating ideas				
Testing out ingredients				
Modelling ideas				
Advertising labelling				
Packaging				
Final recipe				
Promotional photo				

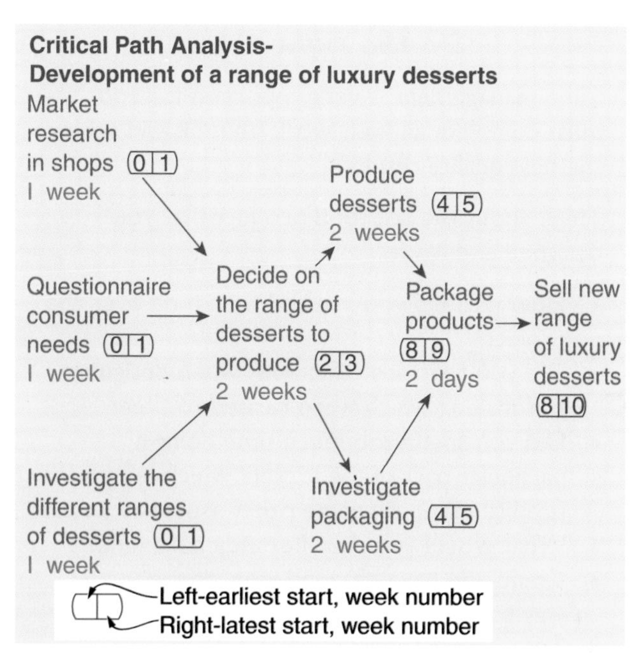

You will find that you will often need to plan in more detail and to allow for a degree of flexibility, so a "Critical Path Analysis" (used in industry) may be used as well.

Making the most of your time

Manufacturers must make the most of the factory plant and equipment so that the business is profitable. They plan the processing of each product carefully to make effective use of their manufacturing team. The production process must be efficient.

Time planning

Do the right thing!

Time management is very important for you. You must complete all your work on time and achieve the best quality results.

Think about the last food product that you designed and made:

- How well did you manage your time over the project?
- Did you have any difficulties when designing and making which were related to time?
- Did you spend too much time doing a particular part of the project which left you too little time on some other aspects?
- What would you do differently next time?
- Could you have changed your design in any way to help you save time?
- Try to learn from your last project. The difficulties you experienced are the same ones faced by the food manufacturers.
- Use the examples of Gantt charts and critical path analysis to help you design your next food product to the schedule that your teacher gives you. Make sure that you allow enough time for each stage.

Focused task: Production system

In small groups set up a production system for the batch production of a product such as a dressing, chutney or sauce.

- Ask another group to evaluate your system
- In return, you will evaluate their system
- Consider factors such as their use of time, how they work in a group, their planning, precision and accuracy.

From your experience, what are the key factors to consider when planning for production?

Food product quality

Making products consistently (so they do not vary in quality from an accepted standard) is very important in the food industry. When you buy a packet of crisps or a frozen beefburger, you have a certain expectation about what you are going to eat. You would not expect a beefburger to be made from chicken. If you open a packet of crisps and find that it is not a full bag, or contains something inedible, you would be disappointed. In other words, you expect a certain level of quality.

The Food Safety Act (1990) ensures that all food products:

- meet all food safety regulations
- have not been contaminated, making them harmful to health
- are of good quality and fit for human consumption
- have been accurately described and presented to the consumer.

Quality assurance

Throughout their manufacturing process, food products are subject to strict **quality checks**, to ensure that the products meet the agreed quality standards. Right first time, every time. This should be distinguished from **quality control** which involves inspection and testing at the end of the process.

Case study: Creating identical products

Manufacture of white-meat products at Birds Eye Walls

One difficulty when aiming for consistently identical products is that raw materials cannot always be guaranteed to be the same size and shape. Where this is the case, particular methods have to be used to ensure consistency. For example, at Birds Eye Walls, chicken used in white-meat products arrives in large frozen blocks with bones and skin already removed. It undergoes quality checks, including microbial and temperature checks, before being placed in the cold store. When needed, the blocks are defrosted in a large scale microwave oven. Flavours and other ingredients may be added and the chicken is fed through a large hopper into a "product former" machine. This is a computer-controlled machine which forms the chicken meat into whatever 3D shape is required.

To create identical shapes, the chicken meat is pushed by a plunger into shaped cavities in a mould plate. The shaped chicken is pushed out of the mould and drops onto the conveyor. It is taken by conveyor to the next stage in the process.

Other raw ingredients can be processed in the 3D former, e.g. at Birds Eye Walls potatoes are made into products like Alphabites and other novelty shapes.

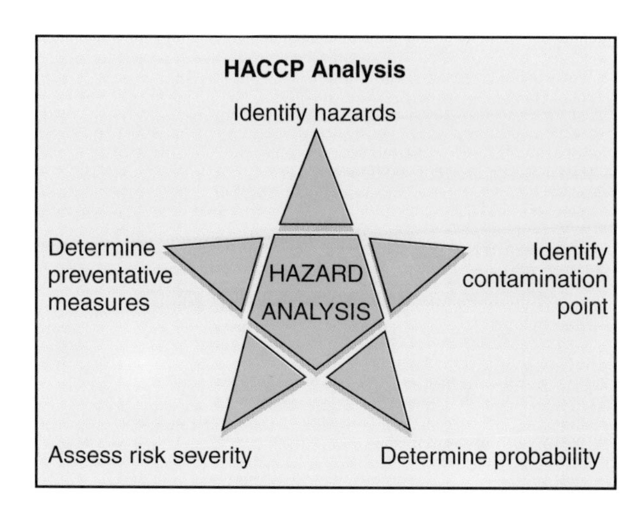

Hazard Analysis of Critical Control Points (HACCP) is one particular quality assurance procedure which is used in the food industry. It takes a systems approach to identifying hazards and risks and defining the means for their control. It may be used during product design, when developing new products and for all processes during manufacture.

As part of the HACCP, an operating manual for each product line is written which contains instructions for all stages in manufacture. This document is a reference point for quality assurance and for training staff to the exact procedures and processes required. The operating manuals will conform to the international standard ISO9000.

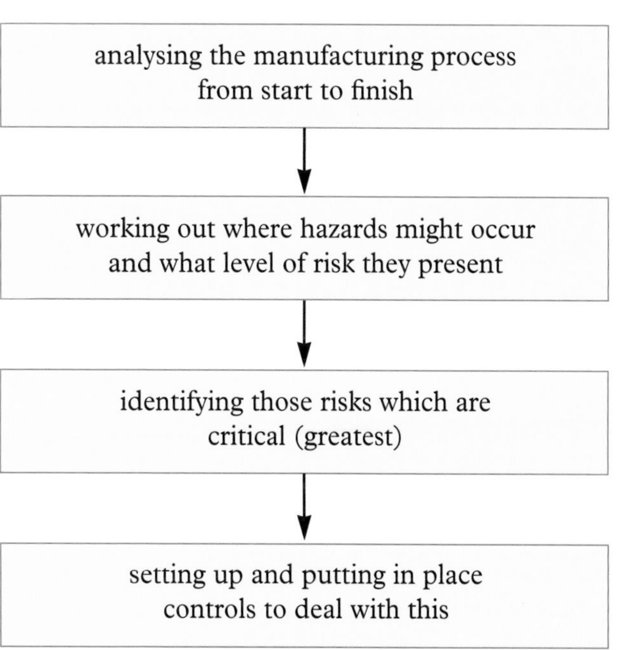

Case study: HACCP system for potato salad

St Martin Food Products Ltd. is based in Southall, Middlesex and supplies airlines and retailers with chilled salads and assembled sandwich products. Its HACCP system has been carefully worked out according to the types of raw materials and manufacturing processes that are dealt with. The factory has been designed and purpose built and it is operated and managed with good manufacturing practice in mind.

Potato salad

Step	Hazard	Preventative measure (CCP)
Receipt of mayonnaise	Contamination by pathogens	Pasteurization
Cooking potatoes	Contamination by *Listeria monocytogenes*	Heat process
Assembly	Recontamination by *Listeria monocytogenes*	High hygiene practices
Packaging	Contamination by pathogens	Adequate sealing
Distribution	Growth of any surviving pathogens	Low temperature storage and distribution within specified shelf life

The chart below shows how part of their HACCP system has been set up. You can see from studying this that a successful HACCP system depends upon identifying risks associated with critical temperatures, times and hygiene practices, and taking measures to control them.

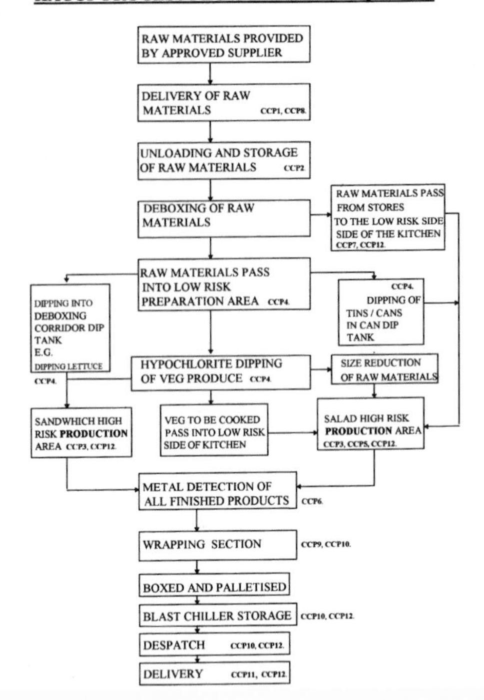

Focused task: HACCP planning

1. Choose a familiar food product, such as a salad, fresh soup, pizza or quiche.
2. Make a list of ingredients and produce a flow chart to show the stages of production.
3. Identify the possible hazards to food safety and mark these on your flow diagram.
4. Identify the critical control points: the points where it is most important to control *any* possible hazards.
5. Plan where you might carry out the necessary quality checks, e.g. visual, temperature.

- What raw materials are used?
- Are micro-organisms likely to be present?
- Will the pH prevent microbial growth?
- Will micro-organisms contaminate the food after it has been heated?
- Would more severe processing be acceptable?
- How does the package affect survival or growth of micro-organisms?
- What is the time taken for each step of processing, preparation storage and display?

You may have some software in school with simple HACCP systems.

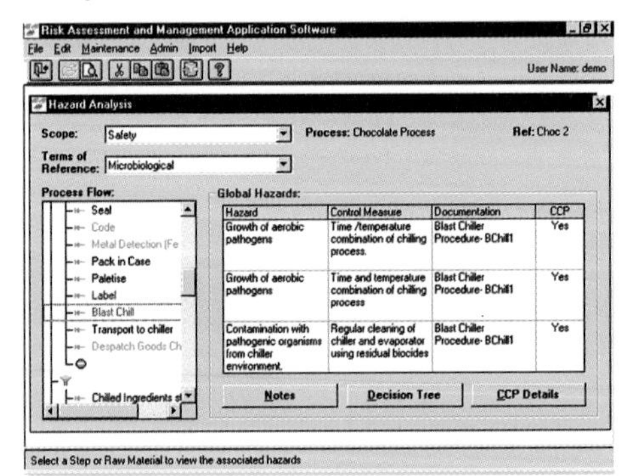

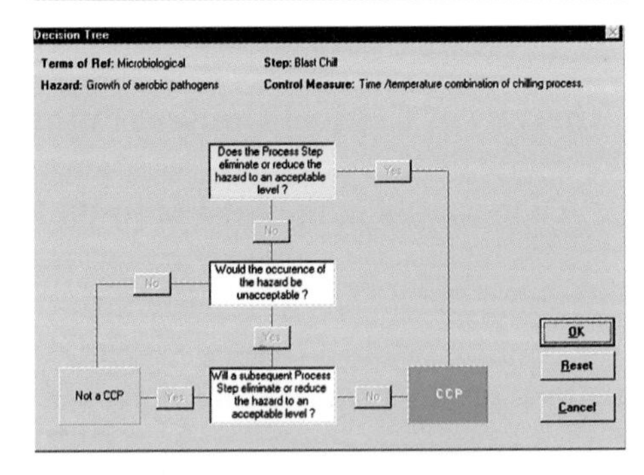

Food hygiene during manufacture

Generally, food becomes unsafe because it has been contaminated. There are three main sources of contamination:

- chemical, e.g. pesticides
- physical, e.g. glass, metal, insects
- microbial, e.g. bacteria.

During food production checks need to be made to ensure that food cannot become contaminated at any stage.

Bacteria can be found everywhere in our environment. Some are beneficial for the manufacture of certain foods, e.g. lactobacillus and streptococcus in cheese and yoghurt. Some, however, are a risk to our health, these are known as **pathogens**, e.g. Salmonella, Clostridium perfringenes.

Cross-contamination is the process of transfer of these organisms. These organisms have adapted to rely on this process to move them around. The items of transfer are called **vehicles**. In food preparation they are generally utensils.

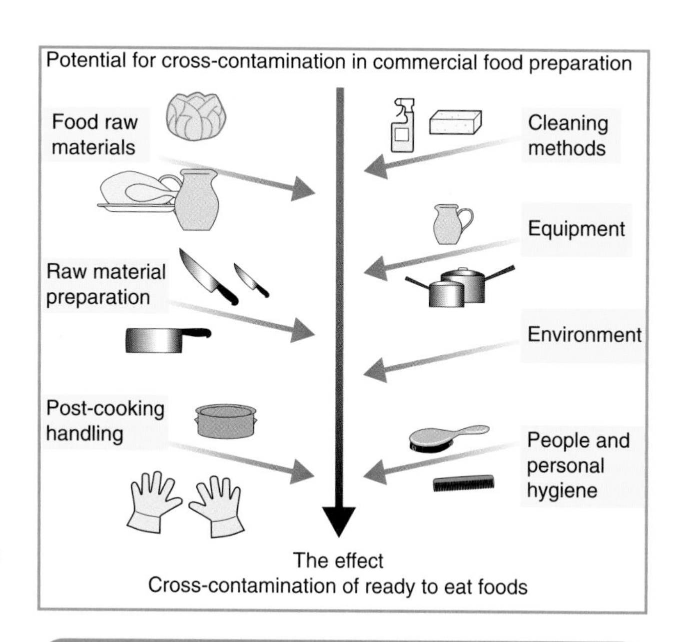

Focused task

A food factory, manufacturing sausages, has appointed a new Quality Assurance Manager. He has sought guidance from an independent hygiene company, to help him develop a hygiene audit, within the factory on a regular basis. Draw up a Code of Practice for the factory with a list of guidelines and recommendations.

Bacterial causes of food poisoning

Type of bacteria	Possible source	Incubation period	Symptoms
Salmonella spp.	raw meat, milk, eggs, poultry and carriers such as pets and rodents, untreated sewage and water	6–72 hours, although usually 12–36	abdominal pain, diarrhoea, vomiting and fever lasting up to a week
Clostridium perfringens	animal and human excreta, soil, dust, insects and raw meat	8–22 hours although usually 12–18 hours	abdominal pain and diarrhoea lasting 12–48 hours
Clostridium botulinum	soil and animal intestines	18–36 hours	lethargy (tiredness and weakness), vertigo, double vision and speech problems
Staphylococcus aureus	human nose, mouth and skin, boils and cuts, raw milk from cows or goats with mastitis	1–6 hours	abdominal pain, vomiting, prostration and below normal temperature for 6–24 hours
Campylobacter jejuni	raw meat, raw milk, untreated water	2–10 days	diarrhoea
Escherichia coli 0157	under-cooked meat, untreated milk	3–8 days	bloody diarrhoea, acute kidney failure

Making use of systems and control

Food manufacturing processes can be considered as a **system**. Systems have **inputs** and **outputs**. A **process** produces the output required, in response to the inputs to the system.

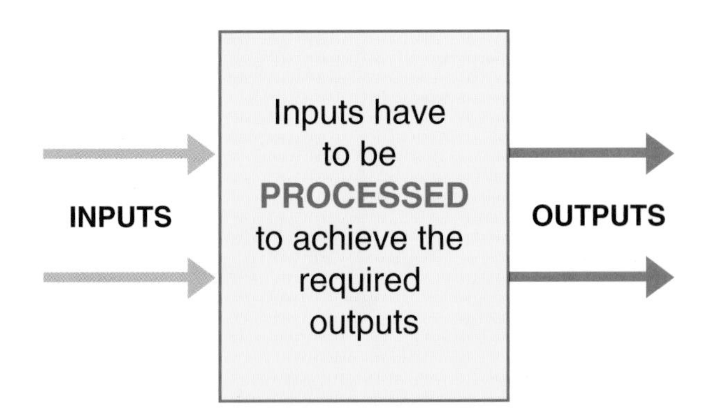

a A system contains a process that produces the required outputs in response to the inputs.

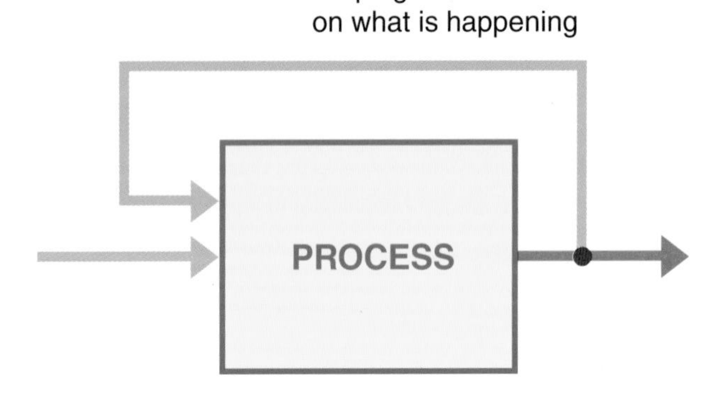

b In many systems, information is fed back from the output to the input. This can be used to monitor or control the system. These are called **feedback** or **closed-loop systems**.

Using a systems approach is a very useful way of analysing complex situations or products. Complex systems can be broken down into a series of smaller **sub-systems**. A supermarket is a good example of a large system made up of many sub-systems. You also need to be clear about where the system boundary is, as this defines the limits of the system you are concerned with.

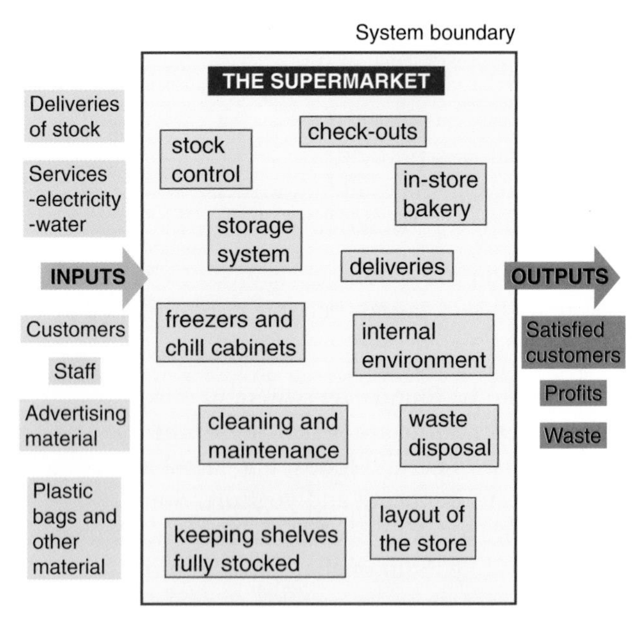

The supermarket system

One useful way of breaking down a complex system is to use an input/output–system diagram. This shows the different stages of the system and how the outputs of one stage become the inputs to the next. You can also see where feedback of information is needed to make sure that the system runs smoothly.

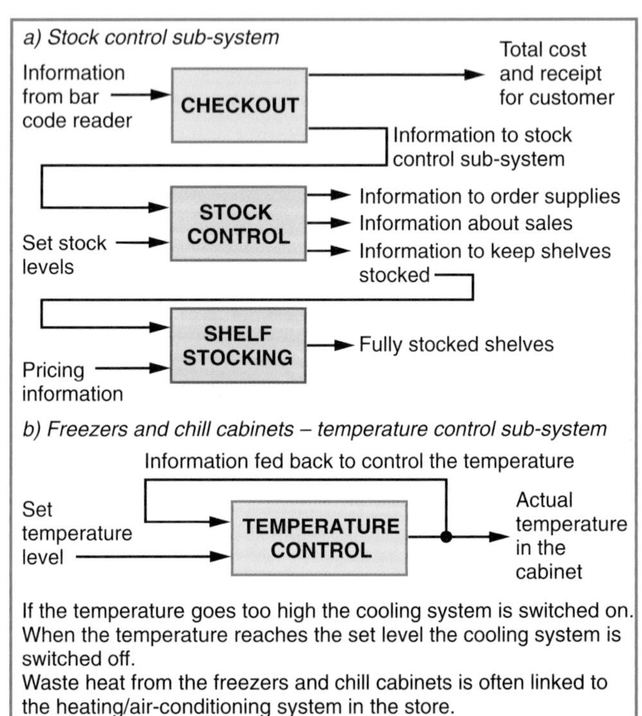

Using input–output systems diagrams to show the links between some of the sub-systems in a supermarket

Flow process charts

Control systems are used in production systems for many reasons:

- repeatability and quality
- using automated systems for tedious, repetitive tasks
- increasing the speed and productivity
- quality control
- safety (e.g. working in hostile environments such as high temperatures)
- reducing waste
- controlling continuous processes
- controlling complex processes
- reducing or removing human error
- reducing maintenance and repair times through the use of warning and safety systems.

Flow process chart	Possible use of control systems
Raw ingredients	
Check quality	
Store raw ingredients	temperature control
Transfer ingredients to processing	materials handling
Process raw ingredients	
Transfer to cooking process	materials handling
Cook	temperature control
Transfer to high risk area	materials handling
Chill	temperature control
Transfer to assembly	materials handling
Assemble	
Quality control	check weighing
Packaging, labelling and coding	
Transfer to storage	materials handling
Store	temperature control

Key ○ An operation ⇨ Transport or movement □ Quality control ▽ Storage

A flow process chart can be used to represent production systems. This chart shows the production of a cook–chill food product.

Case study: Making use of systems

Sainsbury's cook–chill range

Cook–chill is a process that has been developed to preserve the freshness of prepared foods. It is used for fresh soups, fresh pasta, fresh pasta sauces, snacks and ready meals.

A block-flow diagram of the production process

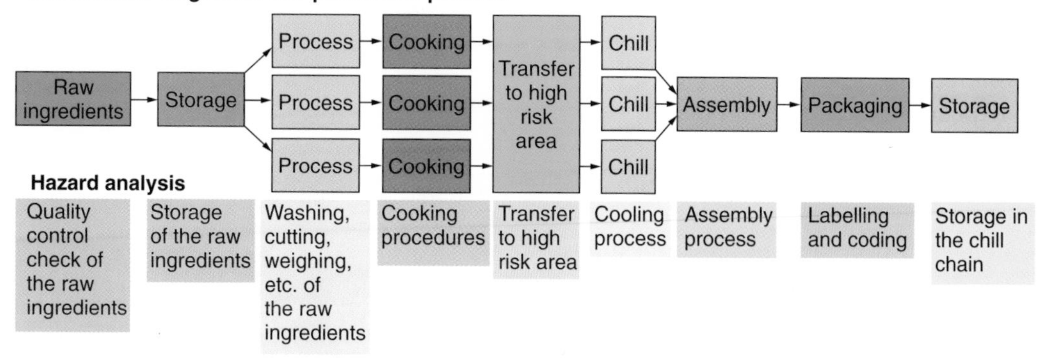

The flow process is broken down into a number of distinct stages for hazard analysis. The analysis is detailed and thorough and carried out to a precise specification.

Focused task

1. Hygiene standards for the cook–chill process are very strict. How can control systems help with this?
2. Look at the block-flow diagram for the production process. Information will be fed back from the assembly and packaging stages to the process stages to make sure that the correct amount of product flows through the production process. At which other stages do you think information needs to be fed back to the previous stages? What information needs to be fed back?

Types of control system

Control systems can involve the use of electrical systems (e.g. heaters), electro-mechanical systems (e.g. solenoids, motors), mechanical systems and pneumatic systems. The processing is usually electronic and often carried out using a computer or microprocessor.

Use this process to help you analyse a situation where a control system could be used.

Making use of systems and control

What do you want to achieve?

Fully describe the task that the system needs to perform and what you want achieve. These questions will help you:

1 What output do you want? What do you want to control? What do you want to happen?
  - What output devices could you use to achieve this?
  - What are the advantages and disadvantages of each?

2 When and how do you want this output to happen?
  - What do you want to cause it to happen?
  - Do you want the system to respond to a change or an event?
  - How can you detect this? What sensing devices could you use?
  - What are the advantages and disadvantages of each?

3 Can the sensing device you have chosen be used with the output device you have chosen? If not, reconsider.
  - If you are designing a control system, do you need feedback control?

4 The information (output) from the input sub-system will need to be processed to achieve the output you require. The type of processing you use will depend on the input and output sub-systems you have chosen.
  - Could you use a computer or micro-processor to control your system?

5 Once you have answered all of these questions, use a systems diagram to show how the sub-systems relate to each other showing the inputs and outputs for each. This means:
  - identifying the inputs and outputs for the overall system
  - identifying any sub-systems
  - identifying the inputs and outputs for each sub-system and the links between them
  - drawing the systems diagram.

6 You can use electronics and other kits to model your system. Using a kit will ensure that the different sub-systems you use will match each other.

Control systems and food manufacture

Control systems are used to monitor and assess the quality and safety of food products and the efficiency of the assembly and production lines. Probes are used to monitor temperature, atmosphere, and pH, as well as the fat moisture content and bacterial count of a product. Sophisticated systems are used to sort, grade, weigh, pack and label products as efficiently as possible. Computerised control systems can be used for rapid detection and identification of micro-organisms, e.g. by X-ray inspection, computer sensors and detectors.

Focused tasks have been included here. If you produce your product in batches, you could consider using these applications of systems and control.

Focused task: Measuring and control

1 Draw a flow chart to map out the unit operations for your product.

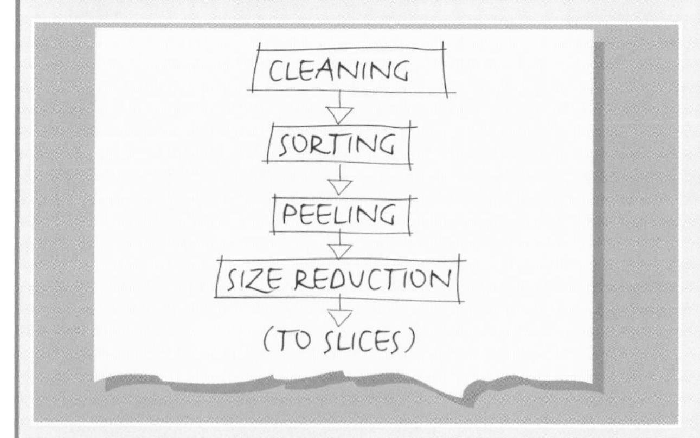

2 Identify the points in your recipe where you could measure time, temperature, pH, texture, weight, size or shape. What equipment could you use to do this?

3 If you were working in industry, you would have specialised equipment to monitor the quality and safety points. Use your flow chart again and suggest the equipment that they would use.

Texture analyser

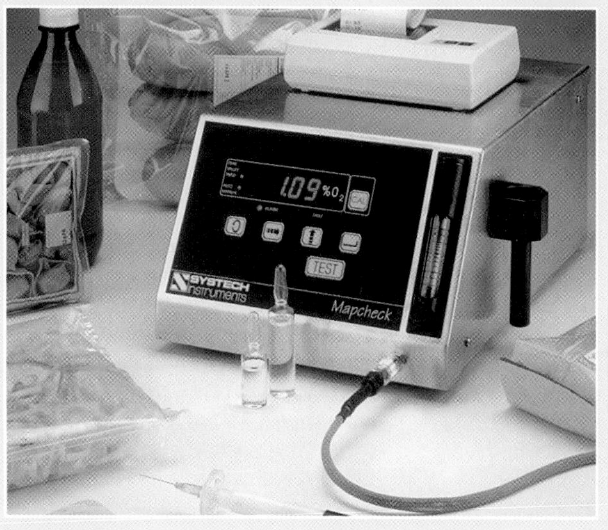

Gas analyser

Making use of systems and control

Focused task: Temperature control

- **Output devices (heaters):**
  12 volt heaters: an aquarium heater is suitable; you may use heaters from your science department, but care should be taken when used with food.
- **Input devices:**
  Thermistors and an integrated circuit temperature sensor (LM35) are the most suitable; you can also buy temperature probes. These can be used with data loggers and a computer to monitor changes in temperature during cooking processes or variations in temperature in different parts of an oven or refrigerator.
- **Processing:**
  In most cases, you will need feedback control. The simplest way of doing this is to turn the heater on and off to maintain the temperature. You can do this using a systems electronics kit.

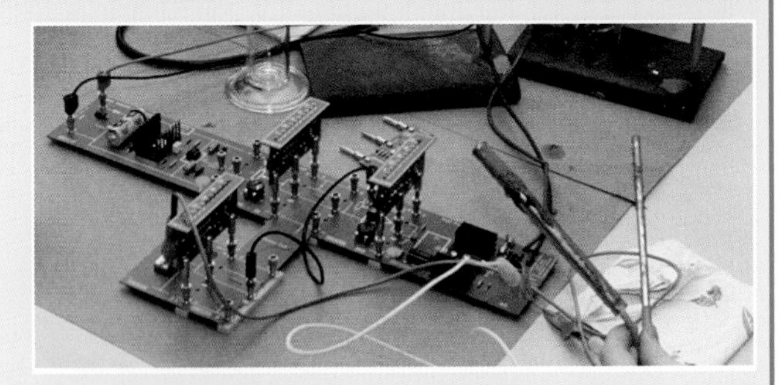

Controlling temperature using ON/OFF feedback control

Focused task: Check weighing

The best way of doing this is to use a **potentiometer**, which provides an electrical signal that can be processed. This means that it can be linked to a number of mechanical devices, such as solenoids and linear actuators, pneumatic pistons and electric motors so that items can be either moved along an assembly line or rejected if required. The potentiometer can be used with a lever system.

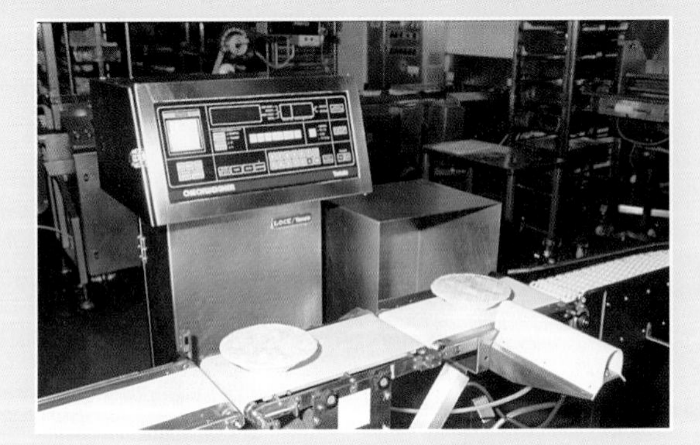

Check weighing. This can be modelled in schools

Case study: Computer integrated manufacture

Decorated cakes

Cake manufacturers may soon be checking the decoration on their cakes with a computer vision system developed at the University of Wales. The system uses opto-electronic scanners positioned above the production line, linked to a computer that processes the digitised video images of the cakes and compares them with images of correctly decorated cakes stored in its database. It is capable of learning from a small sample of decorated cakes what any particular cake should look like.

Focused task: Could you use a computer in your control system?

Computer integrated manufacture is where whole production lines are controlled by computers and monitored by a small number of operators. Are there aspects of your manufacture where you could use computers to help control the process?

Computers can be very useful in control systems. However, they can also cause some problems:

- Computers are not always available and are bulky
- Using a computer might not be the cheapest or easiest solution
- You will need to use a suitable interface with your computer.

Some of these problems can be overcome by using a microprocessor. This "decision tree" will help you work out if it would be useful to use a computer or microprocessor in your control system:

- Make a list of all of the inputs to your control system
- Next to each input write down if it is digital or analogue
- Make a list of all of the outputs from your system
- Next to each output write down which input(s) control it.

Now use the decision tree.

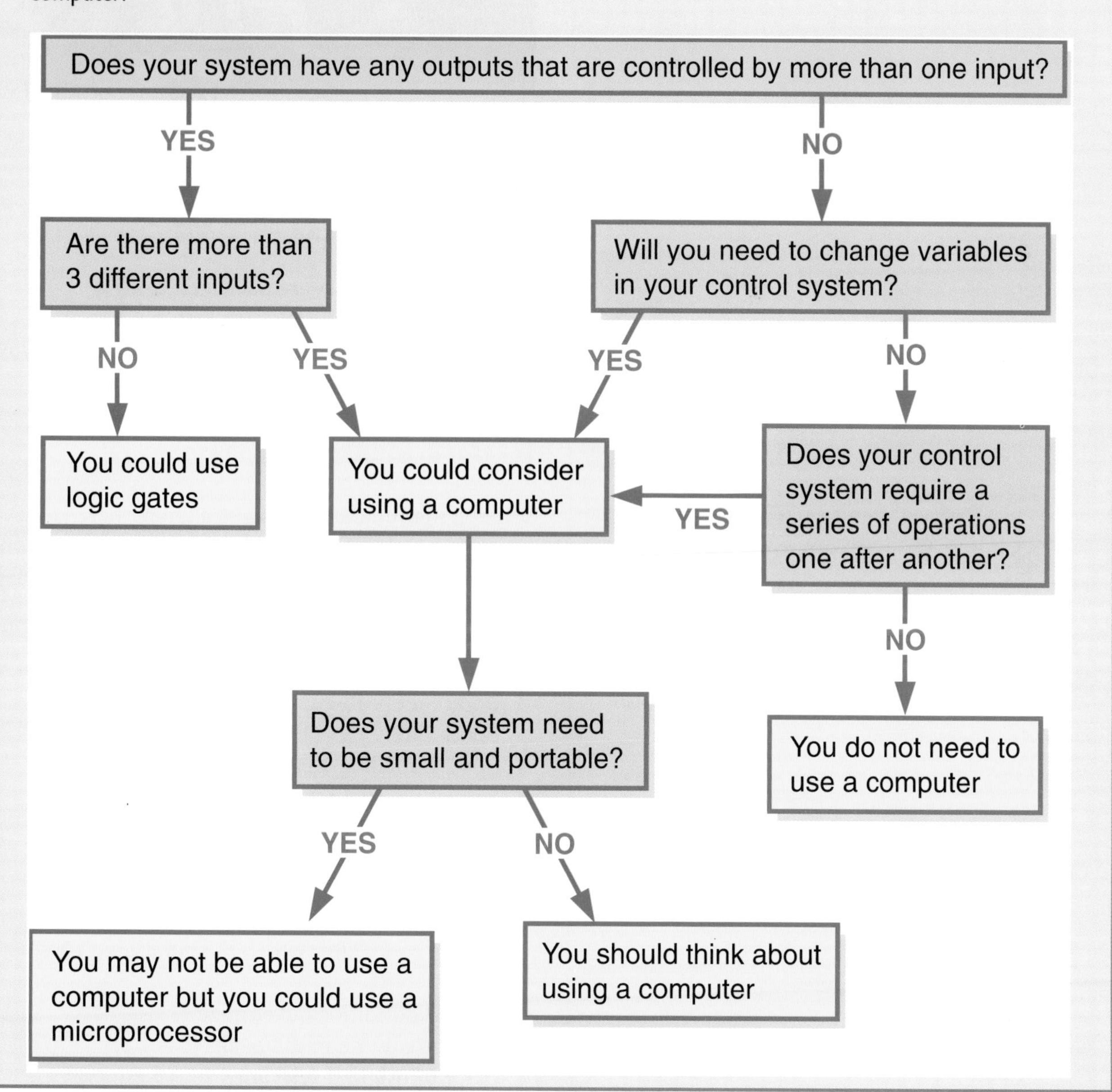

Packaging food products

Some of the fundamental considerations in developing a food package include:

CONTAIN PRESERVE PROTECT

Good packaging means that the quality of the product can be assured once it has been manufactured. Care also needs to be taken of the product during distribution and storage.

Many food products are packaged using a combination of materials, e.g. foil, plastics and cardboard, which are assembled in a variety of ways. Packaging is often a highly automated process.

Focused task

Look at the chart and identify one food product for each group of materials. Explain why you think this material has been chosen for this product.

Packaging material	Properties
Paper and board	No barriers without coatings, good stiffness, absorbent, tear easily, low density, creaseable
Metal	Perfect barrier – if sealed, rigid, high density, can react with foods, needs closures and joints, good tensile strength
Plastics	Wide range of barrier properties, low density, flexible, transparent, tensile and tear strength variable, non-corrosive
Cellophane	Good biodegradability, anti-static, variable permeability, minimal waste, capability of reclosure, high clarity and gloss
Glass	Perfect barrier, rigid, brittle, inert towards foods, needs separate closure, transparent
Cartons	Can be reclosable, versatile, convenient (for modern lifestyles), easy to transport, retains nutrients

Find out what is meant by the following:

a ring pull
b aseptically filled
c hermetically sealed
d tamper evident

Food labelling

When a manufacturer designs a label, there is information that is legally required to be placed on the label.

There are several laws which say what information labels must give:

- Food Safety Regulations (1995)
- Food Safety Act (1990)
- Food Labelling Regulations (1984)
- Sale of Goods Act (1979).

The labels on all food products must contain:

- Name or description of the food
- List of ingredients
- A date code, after which the goods can't be sold
- Special conditions of storage or use
- Weight/volume in the pack
- Place of origin if relevant
- Name and address of the manufacturer, packer or EC seller
- Special preparation or cooking instructions.

Why is new technology used?

The use of new technology in food products has arisen from a combination of the needs of the consumer and the manufacturer's attempts to meet these needs. For example, changes in tastes, preferences and lifestyles have led to a demand for functional foods. These include drinks which are high in fibre and foods low in fat as a result of using carbohydrate-based fat replacers, e.g. food gums.

Novelose is a new starch which has been developed and used to make high fibre snacks, pasta and noodles

There are also cases where the changing pace of technology has an impact on the food industry. For example new processes become possible, existing food materials are used in more diverse ways and new and novel materials can be developed.

Biotechnology

The application of biotechnology has long been used in the production of foods, e.g. in making bread, vinegar, cheese and yoghurt. It involves using biological processes to produce food products. Recently there has been greater use of enzymes and biological organisms in food production. Have you ever wondered why ready prepared Florida Cocktail (Orange and Grapefruit segments) that you buy in the supermarket has no pith on it and all the segments are intact? Does someone spend hours carefully peeling away all the pith? No, enzymes called **pectinases** are used to dissolve away the skins. Another example is bio-yoghurt. This contains active Bacillus cultures which are added to promote the growth of beneficial bacteria in the gut. This is thought to help the digestive processes.

Genetic engineering

The use of new technology in the food industry is controversial, especially products made by modifying or engineering the genetic make-up of food. This might improve the quality of the food, e.g. blackcurrants can be modified to make them higher in Vitamin C, tomatoes can be modified to improve their flavour or keeping qualities. Vegetarian cheese production uses modified enzymes.

Why is new technology used?

Packaging technology

Modified atmosphere packaging (MAP) is a method of packaging foods which extends the shelf life and delays microbial spoilage. It involves changing, or modifying the usual atmosphere which would surround the food. The oxygen in the atmosphere (which is needed for microbial growth) is removed and replaced with carbon dioxide and nitrogen. When kept at low temperatures, it can reduce the need for less popular methods of preservation such as the addition of artificial preservatives. It can be used for a whole range of foods from prepared salads, vegetables and fruit to bread, fresh pasta and meat.

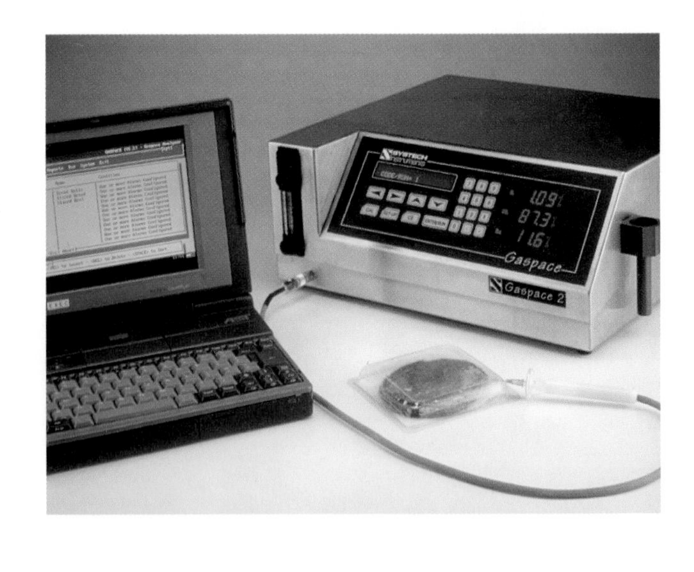

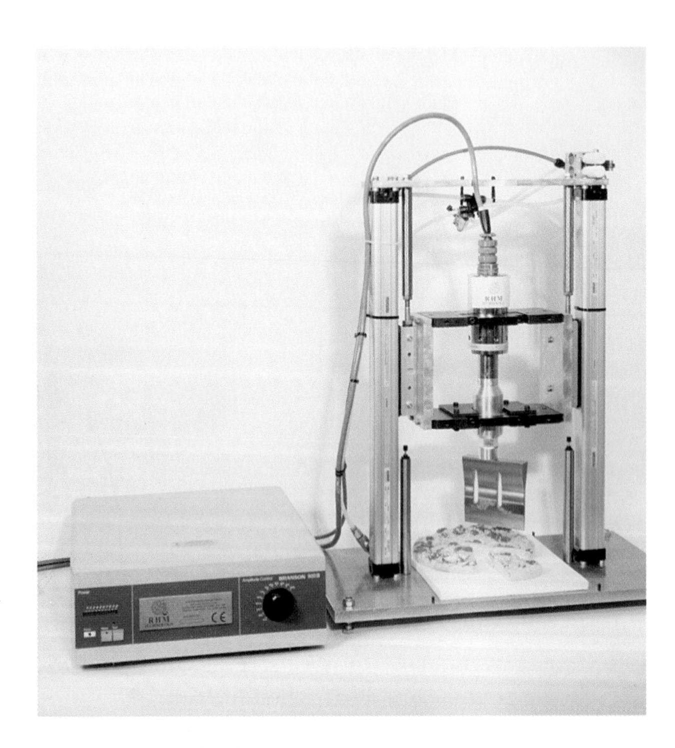

The ultra-sonic knife

The ultra-sonic knife was developed because there were difficulties with dividing cakes on a high speed volume production line. Other portioning methods caused the cake edges to crumble, be ragged or smear, and the cake icing to be dented. The combination of high moisture, different levels of density of the constituents (cake, marzipan, icing) posed severe practical problems. The ultra-sonic knife has a cutting speed of 1.5 seconds. It uses a frequency in the range of 20 kHz. The process appears to make the knife self lubricating.

Ways of heating food

High pressure cooking, ultra-sound, microwave, ultra-violet and **ohmic heating** are all ways of heating foods. Ohmic cooking passes an electrical current through flowing particulate foods, heating them evenly without over-processing. Over-processing usually happens when manufacturers are trying to process foods to safe levels on a large scale. It is a problem because the resulting flavours and textures have not compared well with those of less processed foods.

Use of ultra-sonics

High powered ultra-sound can be used to physically destroy micro-organisms, start chemical reactions or make cell membranes more permeable. It can also be used to aid the tenderising of meats or the dehydration of foods and in the manufacture of margarines.

Focused task: ***What do you think of the use of new technology?***

Not everyone likes the idea that their food may be treated in these ways. Collect newspaper and magazine articles on the use of new technologies in the food industry. Use these to identify the arguments for and against their uses for particular products.

Use of IT in the food industry

IT has many applications across the food industry. It can be used to increase accuracy or precision, to speed up processes and to simulate a variety of functions which might otherwise require considerable time and expertise.

Handling information

Information can be gathered, analysed, sorted or recorded and stored. This may be for research purposes, e.g. to analyse existing market sales, or to find out about particular materials and processes.

Measurement and control

Computerised control systems can be used for rapid detection and identification of micro-organisms, e.g. by X-ray inspection, computer sensors and detectors, all of which results in faster and more accurate quality control.

Modelling

Computers may also be used to identify and simulate food components and closely "copy" original flavours.

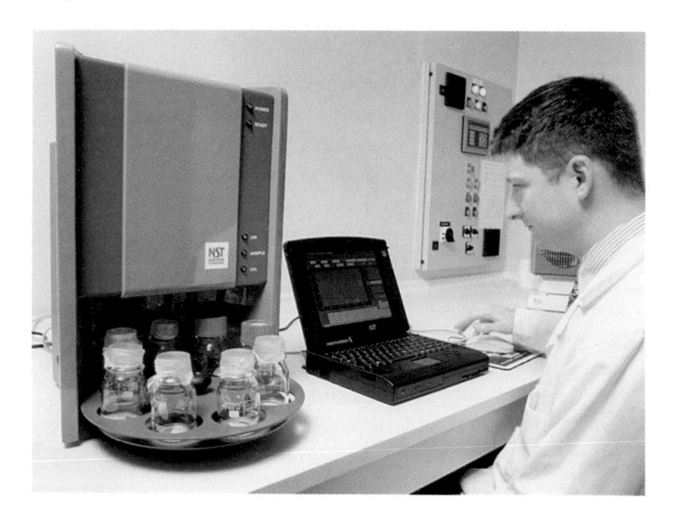

Predicting

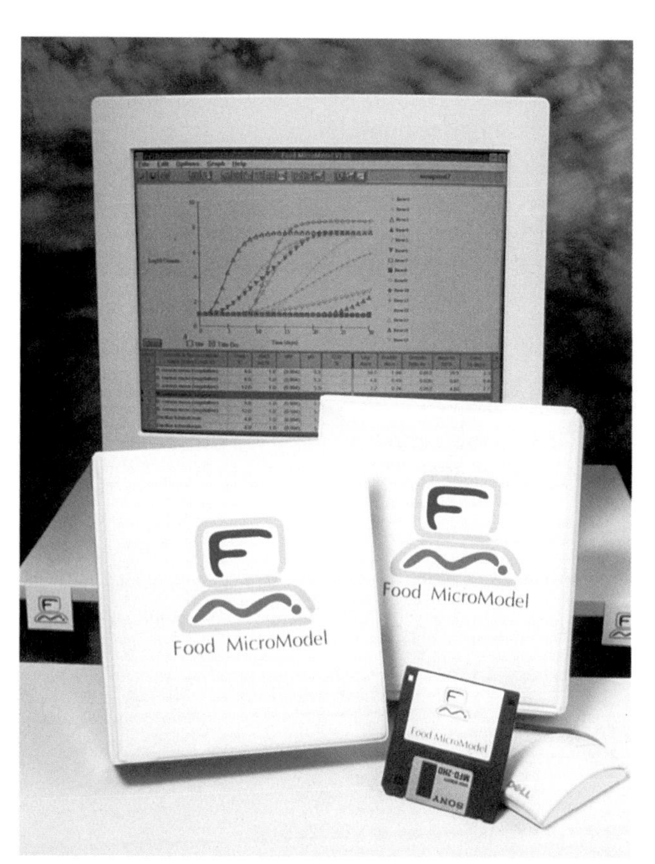

The Food MicroModel is a novel example of a computer software programme used to model bacterial growth in food products. When a new food product is developed, the manufacturer has to be sure that the product created is safe. "Challenge" tests are carried out that include predicting what level and type of microbacterial growth could take place under particular conditions. This can help the manufacturer work out a safe shelf life for the product, and provide the instructions for reheating the product safely and factors such as pH, salt and sugar levels which may need to be reached during manufacture to prevent microbial growth.

Recipes and formulations can be analysed microbiologically. It is then possible to model the effect of changes in formulation and to design safety into a product. This cuts down trial and error in development work, saves times and helps to assure quality for the end product.

The business of manufacturing

There is more to a company than a product and a production line. Somebody has to organise the company, employ and train staff, pay wages, process orders, find buyers, arrange deliveries and so on. It is not enough for a company to manufacture a good product. Managing the different parts of a business properly means getting the **right quantity** of the **right product** to the **right place** at the **right time** to sell at the **right price**.

Who are the manufacturers?

Different kinds of manufacturing are located in every region of the United Kingdom.

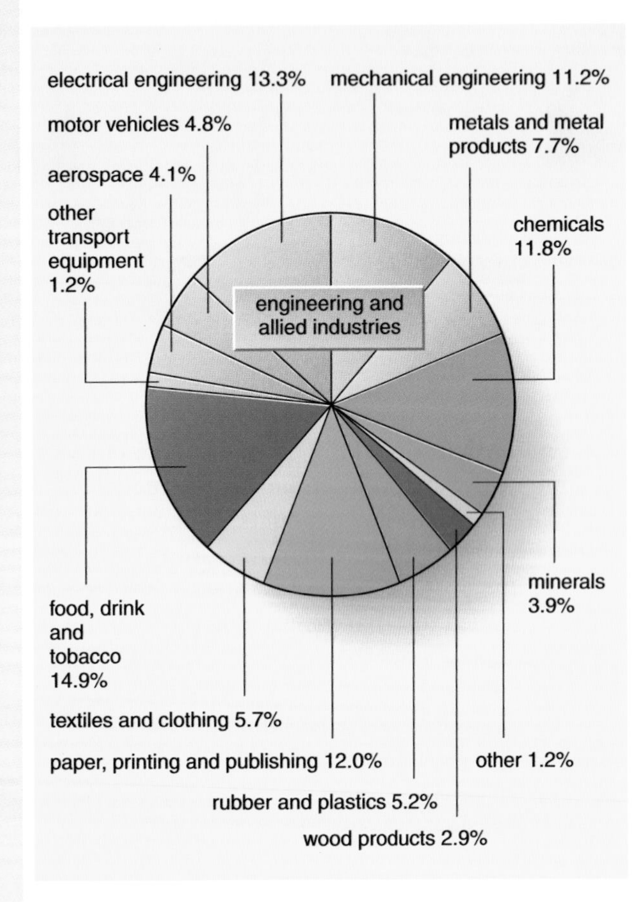

Sectors of manufacturing that use resistant materials, broadly described as "engineering and allied industries", are the largest group. The case study which follows is to help you understand the variety of work that takes place within a manufacturing company. You might compare it with case studies from other sectors of manufacturing contained in the other *D&T Routes* books to develop a broader picture.

Case study: Cauldron Foods

A story of growth

Cauldron Foods began life as a small company manufacturing tofu for the vegetarian market. The founder of the company realised that the demand for vegetarian food was about to take off and saw a gap in the market for a basic food that could be used instead of meat in all sorts of vegetarian dishes.

Tofu is an ancient Chinese food, some 2000 years old. It is made from soya beans. The milk from the beans is extracted and processed into tofu. Tofu can be used as a meat substitute because it has a texture and composition which allows it to be treated in different ways (cut up into chunks, marinated, flavoured, fried, etc.) like meat.

Product innovation

Once a successful base had been created in manufacturing tofu, the managers of the company looked to see how they could expand into new areas of the rapidly growing vegetarian market. They also wanted to make the best use of the food materials they used.

The tofu process produced an important by-product called "okari". This consists of the husks of the soya bean left over once the milk has been taken out. It is very rich in fibre. It was decided to make this into vegetarian pâté. The basic pâté produced proved so successful that it was developed into a full range

The company then looked at how it could produce other vegetarian foods. One of its new developments was vegetarian sausages. It continually reviews its products in the light of consumer feedback to see if it can improve them or add to the range. For these products it buys in supplies from outside.

How is tofu manufactured?

Let's take a tour around the plant to see how the core product of the company is made and how the process is organised.

Raw materials

The soya beans are delivered by lorry to a large container outside the factory. They are thoroughly checked and tested to make sure that they are of a high standard. Then they are put into giant hoppers ready to be delivered into the factory when required.

Processing

The beans are washed, rinsed and ground into a paste. The fibre (okara) is removed. Then it is boiled for 10 minutes at a carefully controlled temperature. The soya milk that is produced is put into curdling tanks where a coagulant (calcium sulphate) is added.

The curd, now much more solid, is fed into a tofu press which forms it into a large solid wedge. This is cut into small portions. These are put into plastic trays which are sealed. The machine which does this also takes out the air and replaces it with a gas which prolongs the shelf life of the product.

Packaging

The sealed plastic trays of tofu are then sent out through a pasteuriser, which cooks them at a controlled temperature. This ensures the safety of the food. They are then cooled and put into pre-printed and date-stamped sleeves. They are packed in boxes and put into a refrigerated store, ready for dispatch to customers.

Quality assurance

A vital part of this whole process is the range of checks that Cauldron Foods carry out to ensure the quality and safety of their products. Most of these are carried out at the company's own laboratory, which is for food safety reasons on a separate site not far away from the main factory. These checks include:

- Testing soya beans on arrival to make sure that they have not been contaminated (e.g. by damaged containers) during their long sea voyage from Canada and are in good condition (not split).
- Testing samples of the cooked milk for the solids content. If it is too high, it can interfere with the coagulation process; too low and it will reduce yields.
- Samples are taken during the process and after it is packed in containers and "microbiologically challenged". These means they are subjected to a range of tests to make sure that the food is safe and that all the cooking processes are working properly. There are also shelf life tests and test for pathogens.

Product development

One of the most important parts of any manufacturing business is the development of new products. These help the company grow and become more successful and profitable. Also, a company which relies on one product can find itself in difficulties if the demand for that product suddenly falls. A company needs to develop a range of products, known as the company's "product portfolio", so that as one product becomes less popular it is replaced by others.

Cauldron Foods has been adding to its product range continually since it began and continues to add new lines. These include different types of tofu (marinated, smoked, basic tofu), vegetable burgers, spicy bean burgers and a range of pâtés and vegetarian sausages.

Continued on page 92

Who works on developing new products?

Some of the key people in the product development team are:

- **Product development manager** Responsible for generating new product ideas. Produces samples in the test kitchen and arranges for these to be tasted. Then supervises the factory trials to make sure that the product is just as good when it is prepared in large volumes.
- **Sales and marketing director** Responsible for research and keeping an eye on competitors' products. Organises sales to customers, often large supermarkets. Also oversees the image of the product in the packaging and arranges sales promotions and advertising to increase sales.
- **Technical manager** Knows about the workings of the factory and the product, and how the two fit together. Understands how the machinery and equipment perform and about product-related issues such as shelf life and microbial spoilage. Can advise on how the sample products can be put into large scale production and help set up the factory trials.
- **Managing director** (MD) Makes sure that the expertise of the different staff is put to full use and that the team of people are working together effectively. The MD is responsible for all the main decisions the company takes especially if they involve large sums of money.

Monitoring the market

The development manager and the sales and marketing director (and other people in the company) constantly look at food magazines and books, TV programmes, and food in restaurants to build up a picture of current trends in food consumption. In particular, they look very hard at the foods produced by their competitors and their own range of foods to see what improvements can be made.

We can look at how Cauldron Foods developed one of their new products to see how the process works. The idea for a new variety of sausages came from a meeting with supermarket buyers. The existing range of Premium sausages were selling well and the market was very lively. So an opportunity to develop a new sausage was identified.

Stop and think

Think about your projects and how you will be taking on most of these roles yourself. Make a note of what you do when you develop a product which is similar to the process at Cauldron Foods. What is not the same?

Developing the Lincolnshire Sausage

The company had recently bought new sausage-making equipment which was not being fully used, so there was some spare capacity. This meant that there would be no need to buy new equipment or to spend money on training staff how to use it. It looked like the proposed product could be produced cost effectively.

The product development process

Research
The development team collected together and tasted all the current vegetarian sausages on the market. They considered the taste and quality of the sausages, and worked out the retail price they would have to charge to compete in the market.

Brainstorming ideas
They took their research findings to a brainstorming session to work out the ingredients and flavours for the new sausage. Then they came up with all sorts of ideas. Two or three emerged as strong favourites, but eventually they refined it to one concept: the Lincolnshire sausage (traditionally made with pork and herbs), which would be: based on a traditional English sausage with a coarse texture; have a more European appeal with vegetables, and a spicy flavour to improve on the flavour and texture of similar

Testing samples

Now it was over to the test kitchen where the product development manager made samples using a variety of ingredients in different combinations. These were tasted and commented on. Then they were improved and tasted again. This process continued until the texture and flavour were considered to be absolutely right.

Presenting to suppliers

The new product was presented to supermarket buyers who liked the final product: a firm and succulent sausage with a coarse texture and a savoury sage and onion flavour. Two major supermarket chains agreed to take it up and sell it.

Manufacture

There was still a lot of work to do before the product could be put into full-scale manufacture. Factory trials had to be carried out to see what would happen when the sausage was produced in large quantities. Sometimes ingredients in bulk behave differently, e.g. herbs can become stronger when used in large amounts. So changes have to be made until the factory product matched the kitchen product. Then it could go into production.

Designing for manufacture

As a product is developed, the following manufacturing aspects have to be taken into account:

1. Costs are kept constantly under review. Spreadsheets are used to monitor costs and see what will happen when different ingredients are used in large volumes. Otherwise the final retail price will be too high.
2. Raw materials are checked so that the right amounts of the right quality can be purchased at the right price.
3. The product development manager has to work closely with the technical and quality assurance managers to make sure that the product will be safe and will have a good shelf life. This means careful monitoring of ingredients and the cooking process (how long the product has to be cooked, and at what temperatures).
4. The production managers and supervisors are involved to make sure that the equipment will do the job and that the new product can be fitted into production schedules. With the other managers, they are an important part of the factory trials.

What does a product development manager do?

You will probably have realised that a key job in the manufacturing business is that of the product development manager. In many ways, this job is not so different from the assignments you carry out in your work. Let's see what this manager does at Cauldron Foods:

- Examines existing products, magazines, books and TV programmes to see what's on the market, current trends and what could be improved
- Brainstorms ideas with other managers to create new product ideas
- Makes test samples.
- Goes through the long process of improving samples by altering the ingredients
- Supervises factory trials by working closely with other managers and staff
- Works with quality control staff to consider technical characteristics of the product: how it behaves during cooking and its shelf life
- Presents new products to buyers
- Helps to prepare the information which goes on the packaging.

Stop and think

How is the work you do similar to this?
What are the main differences?
Why do you need to build an idea of "designing for manufacture" into your work?

Index